Document-Based Activ

HOLT

American Anthem

HOLT, RINEHART AND WINSTON
A Harcourt Education Company
Orlando • **Austin** • New York • San Diego • London

ISBN 0-03-037711-0

2 3 4 5 6 7 8   912   10 09 08 07 06

Contents

Contents

Document-Based Activities

To the Teacher

The materials in this Document-Based Activities (DBA) workbook may be used to reinforce or extend any study of high school U.S. history. Through the source documents contained in the book, students will be introduced to 17 interesting and important topics. Studying and analyzing each group of sources will provide students with opportunities to develop and use their critical thinking skills. The content will expand students' thinking beyond the facts, dates, and events they will learn about in their textbooks.

DBAs are an important part of today's learning environment. To understand the world around them, students need to learn to analyze information as well as the documents that contain them. In addition, high stakes social studies exams are using document-based activities to determine competence in writing and social studies. This workbook is designed to help students develop the skills needed to succeed at answering document-based questions and essays.

OVERVIEW

Each of the 17 activities in this workbook begins with a paragraph of introductory historical background and is divided into two parts. Part A of an activity contains the source materials—which include art, artifacts, primary sources, and secondary sources. Following each source are two questions that direct the student's attention to key information in the source.

Part B of each activity identifies the essay topic (called the "Task"). Part B also reviews the topic's historical background information and introduces writing guidelines.

PROCEDURE

Before students begin Part A, explain that some documents may contain unfamiliar vocabulary. Point out the italicized words that are sometimes listed after **Before You Read**. You may wish to discuss these words or see that dictionaries are available nearby.

When students begin Part B, point out that the essay topic is explained under the heading "Task." Review the writing guidelines listed at the bottom of the page. Remember to remind students that they must use at least four of the sources in part A to get a score of 5.

Students should not need their textbooks to write the essay, but you may prefer to allow students to use them.

SCORING

Carefully explain the criteria you will use to score student work. The rubrics for scoring essays and constructed responses are at the back of the workbook. Focus on requirements such as format, length, paragraph order, a clear introductory paragraph, need for supporting evidence, use of samples, and a strong conclusion.

Document-Based Activities

What are Document-Based Activities (DBAs)?

A document-based activity (DBA) requires you to use a source or a group of sources to produce a written response. DBAs cannot be answered without a careful analysis of source material. Unlike a math problem that you can work out in your head, finding the answer to a document-based activity depends on the use of at least one outside reference.

DBAs are not as difficult as you might think. The idea is to learn to use documents as guides. Sometimes sources help you prove something you already know about a subject. Other times source material guides you to develop a new opinion. Knowing how to examine documents on your own is an important learning tool. Once you've mastered this skill, you will be able to draw interesting conclusions and record them in a clear and organized way.

This workbook contains 17 activities. First you will study a collection of source materials and answer short questions about each one. The documents and questions will help you develop a response to the essay topic at the end of the activity. Some of the documents may contain vocabulary that is unfamiliar. These words are identified in the directions that come before the document.

In the second part of the activity, you will see an essay prompt to which you must provide a written response. And you **must** base your answer on some or all of the source materials. The essay topic is called the "Task" and looks like this example.

TASK Explain the reasons for the rapid settlement of the West that began in the middle of the 1800s.

Following the "Task" is a set of guidelines to help you get started.

Your essay will be scored on a scale of 0–5, with 5 being the highest grade. The rubrics your teacher will use to score your essays and your answers to the short questions are at the back of this workbook.

The most important thing to remember about writing essays for document-based questions is to USE THE SOURCE MATERIALS provided. Let them guide you to an accurate and complete response.

How to Use Primary and Secondary Source Documents

As you study history, you will use a variety of sources to help you understand the past. Primary sources are first-hand accounts of an event, such as diaries, letters, and interviews. Primary sources also include historic documents like the Declaration of Independence and objects that have survived from the past such as coins and stamps. Secondary sources are accounts of past events written some time after they occurred by people who were not eyewitnesses. Your textbook or encyclopedias are examples of secondary sources.

Both types of sources can provide reliable information; both can also contain bias and inaccuracy. It is your job to judge the quality of the sources you encounter in your studies. Here are some tips.

- Read source documents carefully, and re-read if you don't understand the content at first. Underline words and phrases you think are important. State the main idea in your own words. When you come across difficult words or unfamiliar subjects, consult a dictionary or encyclopedia.

- Ask questions like "Who created the source and for what purpose?" and "How much time has passed since the source was created?" Historians use the *rule of time and place* to judge the reliability of source material. The closer a source and its creator were to the time and place of an event, the more reliable the source is likely to be.

- Compare sources with each other. Always use more than one source to confirm the accuracy of information.

- Knowing what to expect from a source will also help. Consider the type of document at hand. Is it a court record or a memoir, a scientific report or an ad? Did the author intend to create a private or public record? Adjust your expectations accordingly.

- Learn to distinguish factual information from opinions. For example, primary sources that are first-hand accounts can make a subject come alive. But they can also be one-sided because they are so personal. Look for vocabulary associated with individual points of view. Words like *personally*, *in my opinion*, or *it seemed like* can signal that the author is stating an opinion or feeling.

As you continue in your studies, your ability to evaluate and use source material will increase. It is sure to be an interesting experience.

Document-Based Activities

Following this step-by-step plan will help you answer document-based questions.

1. **Focus your reading** In some document-based tests, students are told the subject of their essay before they begin reading the source documents. The subject may be called a task, writing prompt, or assignment. Keep this prompt in the back of your mind as you read each source.

2. **Start at the bottom!** Your smartest plan of attack is: read the source line first. Ask yourself who the author or the source of the document is. When was it written? Is it taken from a newspaper, speech, personal diary, or other source?

3. **Evaluate the writer or source** What is the viewpoint of the author? Why is this author writing about this subject? Does the author have a goal or purpose in mind? Is the writer likely to be biased or mistaken for some reason?

4. **Identify the audience** Who is the intended audience or user for this source? Is it the general public? If the audience is a specific group of people, who are they? What interests do they have in common?

5. **Reading a text excerpt** If you see ellipses, or periods in a row, it means that some words or whole sentences have been taken out of an excerpt. This is usually done to shorten a document. Brackets [ ] may have been inserted. Brackets are used to show words that were not in the original document. They are used to help you better understand the information in the document.

6. **Answer the questions** Read the short-answer questions. Expect to re-read the source several times. Always use complete sentences.

7. **Refocus on the essay** Before you move on to the next document, ask yourself: How could this information help me write the essay to come?

Example This is an excerpt from an important source and represents an important time in U.S. history. Practice reading the source line first before you read the excerpt. Notice how much easier it is to understand the speaker's message.

> We have no quarrel with the German people. We have no feelings towards them but one of sympathy and friendship. It was not upon their impulse that their government acted in entering this war . . . We are glad . . . to fight thus for the ultimate peace of the world and for the liberation of its peoples, the German peoples included: for the rights of nations great and small and the privilege of men everywhere to choose their way of life and of obedience. The world must be made safe for democracy . . .
>
> —President Woodrow Wilson in a speech to Congress, April 2, 1917, calling for a declaration of war against Germany

Document-Based Activities

Activity 1

Document-Based Activity

The Revolutionary War

Using Source Materials

HISTORICAL CONTEXT The Revolutionary War began in April 1775 with clashes between American militias and the British. In June the Continental Army was formed under the command of George Washington. Both soldiers and civilians faced hardships as the country struggled for freedom. Americans persevered, however, and eventually formed an alliance with France. In 1781 American and French forces trapped a British army at Yorktown, Virginia. Great Britain then agreed to peace talks and recognized American independence in 1783.

TASK Using information from the documents and your knowledge of American history, answer the questions that follow each document in Part A. Your answers to the questions will help you write the Part B essay.

Part A

DIRECTIONS Examine the following documents and answer the short-answer questions that follow each document.

DOCUMENT 1

> The Connecticut troops will not be prevailed upon to stay longer than their term . . . and such a dirty, mercenary spirit pervades the whole, that I should not be at all surprised at any disaster that may happen. In short, after the last of this month our lines will be so weakened that the minutemen and militia must be called in for their defense; these, being under no kind of government themselves, will destroy the little subordination I have been laboring to establish.
>
> —George Washington, commander of the Continental Army
> Letter to his military secretary, Joseph Reed, November 28, 1775

1. What concerns did Washington have about the soldiers from Connecticut?

_____

_____

2. Why did Washington worry about adding militia troops to the regular army?

_____

_____

Activity 1   Document-Based Activity

The Revolutionary War

DOCUMENT 2

> Sunday Morning Septr, 15 . . . This on the whole was an unfortunate Day to the American States. The loss was owing principally to a Want of Wagons & Horses to remove the Guns and Baggage and to the Situation of the Troops Left behind, and the neglect in the officers, in not forming some proper line of Defence.
>
> The Army was principally called off to the Northward and had been in a State of Retreat from the City for some Days all the Field Pieces had been removed out of the Town and most of the Artillery Companies . . . In such a Situation it was not reasonable to expect that they would make any vigorous Stand. The men were blamed for retreating and even flying in these Circumstances, but I image the Fault was principally in the General Officers in not disposing of things so as to give the men a rational prospect of Defence and a Safe retreat should they engage the Enemy . . .
>
> Monday Septr 16. A large body of the Enemy advanced towards our Lines, Supposed to be three or four Thousand, and a little before Twelve oClock a very Smart and Heavy Fire Commenced between them and our Rangers and riflemen on the Advanced posts. This was sustained by the Rangers Bravely till they were reinforced from the Lines, when the fire grew more sharp and Heavy on both Sides, and continued in the whole for 2 or three Hours, in which Time the Enemy were several Times considerably broken and formed anew, and were finally driven by the Americans about 2 miles, though they were often reinforced. Our men by this Time were much Fatigued, and had some of them almost Spent their Ammunition, and the General Thought best to order them to retreat.
>
> —Benjamin Trumbull, Connecticut militia chaplain
> Journal entries, September 15–16, 1776
> Kips Bay and Harlem Heights, New York

1. According to Benjamin Trumbull, why did the American retreat on September 15 go poorly?

_____

_____

_____

2. How did Trumbull assess the efforts of the American soldiers on September 16?

_____

_____

Activity 1   Document-Based Activity

The Revolutionary War

DOCUMENT 3

Before You Read The following words in the document below may be
new to you: *alluded, entreated, privations*. You may want to use a
dictionary to look them up.

> While we were at Trenton, on the last of December, 1776, the time for
> which I and most of my regiment had enlisted expired. At this trying time
> General Washington, having now but a little handful of men, and many of
> them new recruits in which he could place little confidence, ordered our
> regiment to be paraded, and personally addressed us, urging that we should
> stay a month longer. He alluded to our recent victory at Trenton, told us
> that our services were greatly needed, and that we could now do more for
> our country than we ever could at any future period, and in the most
> affectionate manner entreated us to stay. The drums beat for volunteers, but
> not a man turned out. The soldiers, worn down by fatigue and privations,
> had their hearts fixed on home . . .
>
> The General wheeled his horse about, rode in front of the regiment, and
> addressing us again said, "My brave fellows, you have done all I asked you
> to do, and more than could reasonably be expected; but your country is at
> stake, your wives, your houses, and all that you hold dear. You have worn
> yourselves out with fatigues and hardships, but we know not how to spare
> you. If you will consent to stay only one month longer, you will render that
> service to the cause of liberty, and to your country, which you probably
> never can do under any other circumstances . . ."
>
> The drums beat a second time. The soldiers felt the force of the appeal.
> One said to another, "I will remain if you will." Others remarked, "We
> cannot go home under such circumstances." A few stepped forth, and their
> example was immediately followed by nearly all who were fit for duty in
> the regiment, amounting to about two hundred volunteers.
>
> —A sergeant in the Continental Army, December 1776

1. What problem did General Washington face at the end of 1776?

_____

_____

2. Why do you think the soldiers changed their minds after Washington addressed them
   for a second time?

_____

_____

Document-Based Activity

The Revolutionary War

DOCUMENT 4

Before You Read The following words in the document below may be new to you: *affliction, tributary.* You may want to use a dictionary to look them up.

I Have wrote you 3 Letters since your absence but whether you have ever received one of them I know not. The Post office has been in such a Situation that there has been no confiding in it . . .

"But tis a day of suffering says the Author of the Crisis, and we ought to expect it. What we contend for is worthy of the affliction we may go through. If we get but Bread to eat and any kind of rayment [garment] to put on, we ought not only to be contented, but thankfull. What are the inconveniences of a few Months or years to the Tributary bondages of ages?" These are Sentiments which do Honour to Humane Nature . . .

There is such a Cry for Bread in the Town of Boston as I suppose was never before Heard, and the Bakers deal out but a loaf a day to the largest families. There is such a demand for . . . Rye, that a Scarcity will soon take place in the Country. Tis now next to impossible to purchase a Bushel of Rye. In short . . . there is very little selling. The meat that is carried to market is miserably poor, and so little of it that many people say they were as well supplied in the Siege [the occupation of Boston by colonial forces who were trying to drive out the British during 1775–1776].

—Abigail Adams
Letter to her husband, John Adams
March 8, 1777, Braintree, Massachusetts

1. What hardships did the Revolutionary War create for American civilians?

_____

_____

_____

2. How did Abigail Adams feel about the difficulties she was facing?

_____

_____

_____

Activity 1

Document-Based Activity
The Revolutionary War

DOCUMENT 5

Before You Read The following words in the document below may be new to you: *huzzas, martial, exquisite, inundation, abate.* You may want to use a dictionary to look them up.

Yesterday we celebrated the new alliance [with France] with as much splendor as the short notice would allow . . . the line was formed with admirable rapidity and precision—three Salutes of Artillery, thirteen each, and three general discharges of a running fire by the musketry, were given in honor of the King of France;—the friendly European powers—and the United American States—loud huzzas

the order with which the whole was conducted—the beautiful effect of the running fire which was executed to perfection—the martial appearance of the Troops—gave sensible pleasure to every one present—the whole was managed by signal, and the plan as formed by Baron de Steuben succeeded in every particular, which is in a great measure to be attributed to his unwearied attention and to the visible progress which the troops have already made under his discipline . . .

The General [Washington] received such proofs of the love and attachment of his officers as must have given him the most exquisite feelings—But amid all this inundation of Joy, there is a conduct observed towards him by certain great men which as it is humiliating must abate his happiness . . . I think then the Commander in chief of this Army is not sufficiently informed of all that is known by Congress of European Affairs . . . it should be considered that in order to settle his plan of operations for the ensuing campaign, he should take into view the present state of European Affairs—and Congress should not leave him in the dark . . . he merits an unrestrained confidence.

—John Laurens, aide to George Washington
Letter to his father, May 7, 1778, Valley Forge, Pennsylvania

---

1. Washington's troops spent a hard winter at Valley Forge in 1777–1778. What does this letter reveal about the mood and the fitness of the troops by the following May?

_____

_____

2. According to John Laurens, what difficulty did General Washington face?

_____

_____

Document-Based Activities

Activity 1   Document-Based Activity

The Revolutionary War

DOCUMENT 6

Before You Read The following words in the document below may be
new to you: *obstinate, fortitude*. You may want to use a dictionary to look
them up.

> The battle was fought at or near Guilford Courthouse, the very place from
> whence we began our retreat after the light Infantry joined the Army from
> the Pedee [region around the Pee Dee River]. The battle was long,
> obstinate, and bloody. We were obliged to give up the ground, and lost our
> Artillery. But the enemy have been so soundly beaten, that they dare not
> move towards us since the action; notwithstanding we lay within ten Miles
> of them for two days. Except the ground and the Artillery they have gained
> no advantage, on the contrary they are little short of being ruined. The
> enemies loss in killed and wounded cannot be less than between 6 & 700.
> Perhaps more . . .
>
> The Virginia Militia behavd nobly and annoyed the enemy greatly. The
> horse [cavalry] at different times in the course of the day performed
> wonders. Indeed the horse is our great safe guard, and without them the
> Militia could not keep the field in this Country . . . I am happy in the
> confidence of this Army and tho unfortunate I lose none of their esteem.
> Never did an Army labour under so many disadvantages as They; but the
> fortitude and patience of the Officers and Soldiery rises superior to all
> difficulties. We have little to eat, less to drink, and lodge in the woods in
> the midst of smoke. Indeed our fatigue is excessive. I was so much
> overcome night before last that I fainted.
>
> Our Army is in good spirits; but the Militia are leaving us in great
> numbers, to return home to kiss their wives and sweet hearts.
>
> —Nathanael Greene, general in the Continental Army
> Letter to Joseph Reed, governor of Pennsylvania
> March 18, 1781, from an army camp in North Carolina

1. What was the outcome of the Battle of Guilford Courthouse?

_____

_____

2. What difficulties did Nathanael Greene's soldiers face? What assets did they have?

_____

_____

_____

Document-Based Activity

The Revolutionary War

DOCUMENT 7

Before You Read The following words in the document below may be new to you: *mortification, intrepidity, enfilade, capitulate, artificers.* You may want to use a dictionary to look them up.

Sir, I have the mortification to inform your Excellency that I have been forced to give up the posts of York and Gloucester, and to surrender the troops under my command . . . as prisoners of war to the combined forces of America and France . . .

Although the event has been so unfortunate, the patience of the soldiers in bearing the greatest fatigues, and their firmness and intrepidity under a persevering fire of shot and shells, that I believe has not often been exceeded, deserved the highest admiration and praise. A successful defence, however, in our situation was perhaps impossible, for the place could only be reckoned an intrenched camp, subject in most places to enfilade, and the ground in general so disadvantageous, that nothing but the necessity of fortifying it as a post to protect the navy, could have induced any person to erect works upon it. Our force diminished daily by sickness and other losses, and was reduced when we offered to capitulate on this side to little more than three thousand two hundred rank and file fit for duty, including officers, servants, and artificers; and at Gloucester about six hundred, including cavalry. The enemy's army consisted of upwards of eight thousand French, nearly as many continentals, and five thousand militia. They brought an immense train of heavy artillery, most amply furnished with ammunition, and perfectly well manned.

—Lord Cornwallis, British general
Letter to Henry Clinton, commander of British forces in America
October 20, 1781, Yorktown, Virginia

1. What was Cornwallis's reason for writing to General Clinton?

_____

_____

2. According to Cornwallis, what factors determined the outcome of the Battle of Yorktown?

_____

_____

_____

_____

Activity 1   Document-Based Activity
                                  The Revolutionary War

Writing a Document-Based Essay

HISTORICAL CONTEXT The Revolutionary War began in April 1775 with clashes between American militias and the British. In June the Continental Army was formed under the command of George Washington. Both soldiers and civilians faced hardships as the country struggled for freedom. Americans persevered, however, and eventually formed an alliance with France. In 1781 American and French forces trapped a British army at Yorktown, Virginia. Great Britain then agreed to peace talks and recognized American independence in 1783.

TASK Using information from the documents and your knowledge of American history, write an essay in which you:

- Describe the disadvantages and hardships the Americans faced during their struggle for independence from Great Britain.

- Explain how the Americans met and overcame these challenges to win the Revolutionary War.

Part B

DIRECTIONS Using the information from the documents provided and your knowledge of American history, write a well-organized essay that includes an introduction, a body of several paragraphs, and a conclusion. In the body of the essay, use examples from at least *four* documents. Support your response with relevant facts, examples, and details. Include additional outside information.

GUIDELINES
In your essay, be sure to:

- Address all aspects of the **Task** by accurately analyzing and interpreting at least *four* documents.

- Incorporate information from the documents in the body of the essay.

- Incorporate relevant outside information.

- Support the theme with relevant facts, examples, and details.

- Use a logical and clear plan of organization.

- Introduce the theme by establishing a framework that is beyond a simple statement of the **Task** or **Historical Context**.

- Conclude the essay with a summation of the theme.

Activity 2

Document-Based Activity

Debating the Constitution

Using Source Materials

HISTORICAL CONTEXT In May 1787 delegates met in Philadelphia to revise the Articles of Confederation. By September these men had written a Constitution, thereby proposing a new system of government. Each state then organized a ratifying convention to vote on the new document. Meanwhile, the Constitution was fiercely debated in the press, in public meetings, and on street corners. By July 1788, despite opposition from those who feared that a central government would have too much power, 11 states had ratified the document—two more states than necessary for it to become law. By 1790 all 13 states had approved the Constitution.

TASK Using information from the documents and your knowledge of American history, answer the questions that follow each document in Part A. Your answers to the questions will help you write the Part B essay.

Part A

DIRECTIONS Examine the following documents and answer the short-answer questions that follow each document.

DOCUMENT 1

> The day on which we adopt the present proposed plan of government, from that moment we may Justly date the loss of American liberty . . . why is not the liberty of the press provided for? why will the Congress have power to alter the plan . . . of [choosing] Representatives? why will they have power to lay direct Taxes? why will they have power to keep Standing Armies in time of peace? why will they have power to make laws in direct contradiction to the forms of government established in the Several States?
>
> —David Redick, Pennsylvania Supreme Executive Council
> Letter to William Irvine, supporter of the Constitution, September 24, 1787

1. What does David Redick believe will happen if the Constitution is adopted?

_____

_____

2. What does Redick dislike about the proposed system of government?

_____

_____

Document-Based Activities

Activity 2

Document-Based Activity
Debating the Constitution

DOCUMENT 2

Before You Read The following words in the document below may be
new to you: *retard, coincident, heterogeneous, discordant*. You may want
to use a dictionary to look them up.

The territory of the United States is of vast extent; it now contains near
three millions of souls, and is capable of containing much more than ten
times that number. Is it practicable for a country, so large and so numerous
as they will soon become, to elect a representation, that will speak their
sentiments, without their becoming so numerous as to be incapable of
transacting public business? It certainly is not.

In a republic, the manners, sentiments, and interests of the people should
be similar. If this be not the case, there will be a constant clashing of
opinions; and the representatives of one part will be continually striving
against those of the other. This will retard the operations of government,
and prevent such conclusions as will promote the public good. If we apply
this remark to the condition of the United States, we shall be convinced
that it forbids that we should be one government. The United States
includes a variety of climates. The productions of the different parts of the
union are very variant, and their interests, of consequence, diverse. Their
manners and habits differ as much as their climates and productions; and
their sentiments are by no means coincident. The laws and customs of the
several states are, in many respects, very diverse, and in some opposite;
each would be in favor of its own interests and customs, and, of
consequence, a legislature, formed of representatives from the respective
parts, would not only be too numerous to act with any care or decision, but
would be composed of such heterogeneous and discordant principles, as
would constantly be contending with each other.

—Brutus [pen name of Robert Yates, judge]
Essay 1, October 18, 1787
New-York Journal

---

1. How does Brutus describe the United States?

_____

_____

2. What two reasons does he give for criticizing the idea of a national legislature?

_____

_____

Document-Based Activities

Activity 2

Document-Based Activity

Debating the Constitution

DOCUMENT 3

Before You Read The following words in the document below may be
new to you: *vested, perpetual, prerogative, pretence*. You may want to use
a dictionary to look them up.

> In the first place the office of President of the United States appears to me
> to be clothed with such powers as are dangerous. To be the fountain of all
> honors in the United States, commander in chief of the army, navy and
> militia, with the power of making treaties and of granting pardons, and to
> be vested with an authority to put a negative upon all laws, unless two
> thirds of both houses shall persist in enacting it, and put their names down
> upon calling the yeas and nays for that purpose, is in reality to be a KING
> as much *a King as the King of Great-Britain,* and a King too of the worst
> kind;—an elective King . . . The election of a King whether it be in
> America or Poland, will be a scene of horror and confusion; and I am
> perfectly serious when I declare that, as a friend to my country, I shall
> despair of any happiness in the United States until this office is either
> reduced to a lower pitch of power or made perpetual and hereditary.—
> When I say that our future President will be as much a king as the king of
> Great-Britain, I only ask of my readers to look into the constitution of that
> country, and then tell me what important prerogative the King of Great-
> Britain is entitled to, which does not also belong to the President during his
> continuance in office . . .
>
> If we are not prepared to *receive a king*, let us call another convention to
> revise the proposed constitution, and form it anew on the principles of a
> confederacy of free republics; but by no means, under pretence of a
> republic, to lay the foundation for a military government, which is the
> worst of all tyrannies.
>
> —An Old Whig
Essay V, November 1, 1787
Independent Gazetteer, Philadelphia

1. What flaw does the author find in the proposed Constitution? How does he support
   his argument?

   _____

   _____

2. What changes to the proposed system of government does the author suggest?

   _____

   _____

Document-Based Activities

Document-Based Activity

Debating the Constitution

DOCUMENT 4

Before You Read The following words in the document below may be
new to you: *insurgency, impunity, abetted, candor.* You may want to use a
dictionary to look them up.

> The constitution has labored in Massachusetts exceedingly more than was
> expected. The opposition has not arisen from a consideration of the merits
> or demerits of the thing itself, as a political machine, but from a deadly
> principle levelled at the existence of all government whatever. The
> principle of insurgency expanded, deriving fresh strength and life from the
> impunity with which the rebellion of last year was suffered to escape. It is
> a singular circumstance, that in Massachusetts the property, the ability, and
> the virtue of the State, are almost solely in favor of the constitution.
> Opposed to it are the late insurgents, and all those who abetted their
> designs, constituting four fifths of the opposition. A few, very few indeed,
> well meaning people are joined to them. The friends of the constitution in
> that State, without overrating their own importance, conceived that the
> decision of Massachusetts would most probably settle the fate of the
> proposition. They therefore proceeded most cautiously and wisely, debated
> every objection with the most guarded good nature and candor, but took no
> questions on the several paragraphs, and thereby prevented the
> establishment of parties. This conduct has been attended with the most
> beneficial consequences.
>
> —Henry Knox, Secretary of War
> Letter to George Washington, February 10, 1788

1. According to Secretary of War Knox, why do the "insurgents" in Massachusetts
   oppose the Constitution?

   _____

   _____

   _____

2. How does Knox describe the character and conduct of those in the state who support
   the Constitution?

   _____

   _____

   _____

Activity 2   Document-Based Activity
_____
                                         Debating the Constitution

DOCUMENT 5

Before You Read The following word in the second document below may
be new to you: *abated*. You may want to use a dictionary to look it up.

Before we establish a government, whose acts will be THE SUPREME LAW OF
THE LAND, and whose power will extend to almost every case without
exception, we ought carefully to guard ourselves by a BILL OF RIGHTS,
against the invasion of those liberties which it is essential for us to retain,
which it is of no real use to government to strip us of; but which in the
course of human events have been too often insulted.

> —An Old Whig
> Essay IV, October 27, 1787
> *Independent Gazetteer*, Philadelphia

Yesterday our Assembly were to meet and I suppose they will be able to
make a House next week. It is expected by the Anti-Federalist Party that
very extensive Petitions will be laid before them against the new
Constitution. I however think they have abated very much in their Warmth
since they see Massachusetts have come into it . . . And they at last say
they think amendments will probably be made. I sincerely hope they will,
as it would be a means of reconciling all Party's, and enable us to carry it
through; Without them, the opposition will be so powerful as to clog its
execution in too great a degree.

> —Walter Stewart, Philadelphia merchant
> Letter to fellow Pennsylvanian William Irvine
> on efforts by some in the Pennsylvania state assembly
> to overturn Pennsylvania's ratification of the Constitution
> February 20, 1788

---

1. What is the position of each writer about a Bill of Rights?

   _____

   _____

   _____

2. Massachusetts ratified the Constitution on February 6, 1788. According to Walter
   Stewart, how did this affect the situation in Pennsylvania?

   _____

   _____

Document-Based Activity
Debating the Constitution

DOCUMENT 6

Before You Read The following words in the document below may be new to you: *enumerated*, *equivocal*, *dissent*, *sophistry*. You may want to use a dictionary to look them up.

> Congratulations on the acceptance of the new constitution by the State of Massachusetts. Had this been done . . . by a larger majority, the stroke would have been more severely felt by the antifederalists in other States. As it is, it operates as a damper to their hopes, and is a matter of disappointment and chagrin to them all.
>
> Under the circumstances enumerated in your letters, the favorable decision, which has taken place in that State, could hardly have been expected. Nothing less than the good sense, sound reasoning, moderation, and temper of the supporters of the measure could have carried the question. It will be very influential on the equivocal States. In the two, which are next to convene, New Hampshire and Maryland, there can be no doubt of its adoption, and in South Carolina but little, which will make nine States without a dissentient. The force of this argument is hardly to be resisted by local sophistry. Candor and prudence, therefore, it is to be hoped will prevail; and yet I believe there are some characters among us, who would hazard everything rather than cease their opposition.
>
> —George Washington
> Letter to Henry Knox, Secretary of War
> March 3, 1788

1. How does George Washington account for the decision in Massachusetts to ratify the Constitution?

_____

_____

_____

_____

2. What does Washington predict will happen regarding the Constitution?

_____

_____

_____

_____

Activity 2

Document-Based Activity

Debating the Constitution

DOCUMENT 7

Before You Read The following words in the document below may be
new to you: *replete, confute, dispatch.* You may want to use a dictionary to
look them up.

> I congratulate you my fellow-citizens on the ratification of the new
> constitution. This event, replete with advantages, promises to repay us for
> the toils, dangers and waste of the late revolution. Merely to have
> established independence was but half the work assigned to this generation.
> Without an efficient government to protect our rights, in vain have our
> heroes spilt their blood in emancipating us from Great-Britain . . .
>
> Had not the present constitution, or something equivalent been adopted,
> no one can compute the confusion and disorder which would probably
> have taken place from the jarring interests of such an ungoverned
> multitude. The articles of confederation were of too feeble a texture to bind
> us together, or to ward off threatened evils . . .
>
> We have now in our view the fairest prospects of political happiness; the
> wisdom, energy and well poised ballances of our new system, promise to
> confute the assertions of those who maintain "that there are incurable evils
> inherent in every form of republican government." From the federal house
> of representatives we may expect a sympathy with the wants and wishes of
> the people—from the senate, wisdom, unity of design and a permanent
> system of national happiness.—from the executive, secrecy, vigor and
> dispatch. In short, our new constitution is a happy combination of the
> simple forms of government and as free from the inconveniences of each,
> as could be expected . . . It unites liberty with safety, and promises the
> enjoyment of all the rights of civil society, while it leads us up the steep
> ascent to national greatness.
>
> —David Ramsay, delegate to the South Carolina ratifying convention
> Speech in Charleston, South Carolina, June 5, 1788

1. What does Ramsay say would have happened had the Constitution not been adopted?

_____

_____

2. How does Ramsay assess the system of government created by the Constitution?

_____

_____

_____

Document-Based Activities

Activity 2

Document-Based Activity

Debating the Constitution

Writing a Document-Based Essay

HISTORICAL CONTEXT In May 1787 delegates met in Philadelphia to revise the Articles of Confederation. By September these men had written a Constitution, thereby proposing a new system of government. Each state then organized a ratifying convention to vote on the new document. Meanwhile, the Constitution was fiercely debated in the press, in public meetings, and on street corners. By July 1788, despite opposition from those who feared that a central government would have too much power, 11 states had ratified the document—two more states than necessary for it to become law. By 1790 all 13 states had approved the Constitution.

TASK Using information from the documents and your knowledge of American history, write an essay in which you:

- Explain why some Americans opposed the Constitution.

- Discuss how supporters of the Constitution won the battle for ratification.

Part B

DIRECTIONS Using the information from the documents provided and your knowledge of American history, write a well-organized essay that includes an introduction, a body of several paragraphs, and a conclusion. In the body of the essay, use examples from at least *four* documents. Support your response with relevant facts, examples, and details. Include additional outside information.

GUIDELINES
In your essay, be sure to:

- Address all aspects of the **Task** by accurately analyzing and interpreting at least *four* documents.

- Incorporate information from the documents in the body of the essay.

- Incorporate relevant outside information.

- Support the theme with relevant facts, examples, and details.

- Use a logical and clear plan of organization.

- Introduce the theme by establishing a framework that is beyond a simple statement of the **Task** or **Historical Context**.

- Conclude the essay with a summation of the theme.

Document-Based Activities

Activity 3 _____

Document-Based Activity
The Second Great Awakening

Using Source Materials

HISTORICAL CONTEXT In 1801 a series of large, outdoor, religious meetings were held in Kentucky. Mass revivals later spread through the other western states. In the 1820s and 1830s preachers such as Charles Finney promoted revivalism in western New York and other parts of the Northeast. The movement became known as the Second Great Awakening. Religious passion intensified. Church membership soared. The Awakening also helped spark an era of social reform. Americans moved by spiritual fervor became a force for cultural change in the mid-1800s.

TASK Using information from the documents and your knowledge of American history, answer the questions that follow each document in Part A. Your answers to the questions will help you write the Part B essay.

Part A

DIRECTIONS Examine the following documents and answer the short-answer questions that follow each document.

DOCUMENT 1

> The meeting was protracted for weeks. Ministers of almost all denominations flocked in from far and near. The meeting was kept up by night and day. Thousands heard of the mighty work, and came on foot, on horseback, in carriages and wagons . . . From this camp-meeting . . . the news spread through all the Churches, and through all the land, and it excited great wonder and surprise; but it kindled a religious flame that spread all over Kentucky and through many other states.
>
> —Description of a camp meeting in Cane Ridge, Kentucky, 1801
> *Autobiography of Peter Cartwright, The Backwoods Preacher*

1. Who attended the camp meeting at Cane Ridge?

_____

_____

2. How does Cartwright assess the impact of the camp meeting?

_____

_____

Activity 3

Document-Based Activity
The Second Great Awakening

DOCUMENT 2

Before You Read The following words in the document below may be new to you: *depravity, sanctification, penitents, ere, incessant.* You may want to use a dictionary to look them up.

It was in the course of this summer that I found the opportunity I had long wished for, of attending a camp-meeting . . . this was in a wild district in the confines of Indiana . . .

At midnight a horn sounded through the camp, which, we were told, was to call the people from private to public worship; and we presently saw them flocking from all sides to the front of the preachers' stand . . . There were about two thousand persons assembled.

One of the preachers began in a low nasal tone, and, like all other Methodist preachers, assured us of the enormous depravity of man as he comes from the hands of his Maker, and of his perfect sanctification after he had wrestled sufficiently with the Lord to get hold of him . . .

The preachers came down from their stand and placed themselves in the midst of it, beginning to sing a hymn, calling upon the penitents to come forth. As they sang they kept turning themselves round to every part of the crowd, and, by degrees, the voices of the whole multitude joined in chorus . . . but ere I had well enjoyed it, the scene changed . . .

Above a hundred persons, nearly all females, came forward, uttering howlings and groans, so terrible that I shall never cease to shudder when I recall them. They appeared to drag each other forward, and on the word being given, "let us pray," they all fell on their knees . . . they were soon all lying on the ground in an indescribable confusion of heads and legs. They threw about their limbs with such incessant and violent motion, that I was every instant expecting some serious accident to occur.

—Frances Trollope, English traveler in America
Domestic Manners of the Americans, 1832

---

1. What was the message of the preacher's sermon?

   _____

   _____

2. Why do you think some people at this camp meeting howled, groaned, and flailed on the ground?

   _____

   _____

Activity 3

Document-Based Activity
The Second Great Awakening

DOCUMENT 3

Before You Read The following words in the document below may be
new to you: *backslidden, profligates, harlots, infidels.* You may want to
use a dictionary to look them up.

There is so little principle in the church, so little firmness and stability of
purpose, that unless the religious feelings are awakened and kept excited,
counter worldly feeling and excitement will prevail, and men will not obey
God . . . The state of the world is still such, and probably will be till the
millennium is fully come, that religion must be mainly promoted by means
of revivals . . .

   1. A revival always includes conviction of sin on the part of the church.
Backslidden professors cannot wake up and begin right away in the service
of God, without deep searchings of heart . . .

   2. Backslidden Christians will be brought to repentance. A revival is
nothing else than a new beginning of obedience to God. Just as in the case
of a converted sinner, the first step is a deep repentance, a breaking down
of heart, a getting down into the dust before God, with deep humility, and
forsaking of sin.

   3. Christians will have their faith renewed . . . They will feel grieved that
others do not love God, when they love him so much. And they will set
themselves feelingly to persuade their neighbors to give him their hearts. . .
They will have a longing desire for the salvation of the whole world . . .

   5. When the churches are thus awakened and reformed, the reformation
and salvation of sinners will follow . . . Very often the most abandoned
profligates are among the subjects. Harlots, and drunkards, and infidels,
and all sorts of abandoned characters, are awakened and converted. The
worst part of human society are softened, and reclaimed, and made to
appear as lovely specimens of the beauty of holiness.

                       —Charles Finney, revivalist minister
                 Lectures on the Revivals of Religion, 1835

---

1. What criticisms does Charles Finney make regarding the church?

_____

_____

2. How does Finney suggest that revivals can have a larger social impact on America?

_____

_____

Activity 3   Document-Based Activity

The Second Great Awakening

DOCUMENT 4

Before You Read The following words in the document below may be
new to you: *execrate, intemperance, lazar, ardent, proscribed.* You may
want to use a dictionary to look them up.

We execrate the cruelties of the slave trade—the husband torn from the
bosom of his wife—the son from his father—brothers and sisters separated
forever—whole families in a moment ruined! But are there no similar
enormities to be witnessed in the United States? None indeed perpetrated
by the bayonet—but many, very many, perpetrated by intemperance.

Every year thousands of families are robbed of fathers, brothers,
husbands, friends. Every year widows and orphans are multiplied, and grey
hairs are brought with sorrow to the grave—no disease makes such inroads
upon families, blasts so many hopes, destroys so many lives, and causes so
many mourners to go about the streets . . .

We have heard of the horrors of the middle passage—the transportation
of slaves—the chains—the darkness—the stench—the mortality and living
madness of woe—and it is dreadful. But bring together the victims of
intemperance, and crowd them into one vast lazar-house, and sights of woe
quite as appalling would meet your eyes . . .

The commerce therefore, in ardent spirits, which produces no good, and
produces a certain and an immense amount of evil, must be regarded as an
unlawful commerce, and ought, upon every principle of humanity, and
patriotism, and conscience, and religion, to be abandoned and proscribed.

—Lyman Beecher, Presbyterian minister
Six Sermons on Intemperance, 1827

---

1. How does Lyman Beecher compare intemperance with the slave trade?

_____

_____

_____

2. What change is Beecher calling for?

_____

_____

_____

Activity 3

Document-Based Activity
The Second Great Awakening

DOCUMENT 5

Before You Read The following words in the document below may be new to you: *adjudicated, begotten.* You may want to use a dictionary to look them up.

> The case of Human Rights against Slavery has been adjudicated in the court of conscience times innumerable. The same verdict has always been rendered—"Guilty;" the same sentence has always been pronounced, "Let it be accursed;" and human nature, with her million echoes, has rung it round the world in every language under heaven, "Let it be accursed. Let it be accursed." . . . There is not a man on earth who does not believe that slavery is a curse. Human beings may be inconsistent, but human *nature* is true to herself. She has uttered her testimony against slavery with a shriek ever since the monster was begotten . . .
>
> We will prove that the slaves in the United States are treated with barbarous inhumanity; that they are overworked, underfed, wretchedly clad and lodged, and have insufficient sleep; that they are often made to wear round their necks iron collars armed with prongs, to drag heavy chains and weights at their feet while working in the field, and to wear yokes . . . that they are often kept confined in the stocks day and night for weeks together, made to wear gags in their mouths for hours or days, have some of their front teeth torn out or broken off, that they may be easily detected when they run away; that they are frequently flogged with terrible severity . . .
>
> Reader, what have you to say of such treatment? Is it right, just, benevolent? Suppose I should seize you, rob you of your liberty, drive you into the field, and make you work without pay as long as you live, would that be justice and kindness, or monstrous injustice and cruelty?
>
> —Theodore Weld, revivalist minister and abolitionist
> *American Slavery as It Is*, 1839

1. According to Theodore Weld, what is the condition of slaves in the United States?

_____

_____

2. Does Weld use legal, religious, or moral reasoning to make the case that slavery is wrong? Explain.

_____

_____

_____

Activity 3

Document-Based Activity

The Second Great Awakening

DOCUMENT 6

Before You Read The following words in the document below may be new to you: *reverence, endeavor, naught, Jehovah.* You may want to use a dictionary to look them up.

In every man's mind the good seeds of liberty are planted, and he who brings his fellow down so low, as to make him contented with a condition of slavery, commits the highest crime against God and man. Brethren, your oppressors aim to do this. They endeavor to make you as much like brutes as possible. When they have blinded the eyes of your mind—when they have embittered the sweet waters of life—when they have shut out the light which shines from the word of God—then, and not till then has American slavery done its perfect work.

TO SUCH DEGRADATION IT IS SINFUL IN THE EXTREME FOR YOU TO MAKE VOLUNTARY SUBMISSION. The divine commandments, you are in duty bound to reverence, and obey. If you do not obey them you will surely meet with the displeasure of the Almighty He requires you to love him supremely, and your neighbor as yourself—to keep the Sabbath day holy—to search the Scriptures—and bring up your children with respect for his laws, and to worship no other God but him. But slavery sets all these at naught and hurls defiance in the face of Jehovah . . .

Brethren, the time has come when you must act for yourselves. It is an old and true saying, that "if hereditary bondmen would be free, they must themselves strike the blow." You can plead your own cause, and do the work of emancipation better than any others.

—Henry Highland Garnet, African American minister
An Address to the Slaves of the United States, 1843

1. How does Henry Garnet use religion as part of his argument against slavery?

_____

_____

_____

2. What do you think Garnet had in mind when he encouraged slaves to "act for yourselves"?

_____

_____

_____

Activity 3

Document-Based Activity
The Second Great Awakening

DOCUMENT 7

Before You Read The following word in the document below may be new to you: *fettered*. You may want to use a dictionary to look it up.

> You seem greatly alarmed at the idea of our advocating the rights of woman . . .
>
> Can you not see that women could do, and would do a hundred times more for the slave if she were not fettered? Why! We are gravely told that we are out of our sphere even when we circulate petitions; out of our "appropriate sphere" when we speak to women only; and out of it when we sing in the churches. Silence is our province, submission our duty . . . If we are to do any good in the Anti Slavery cause, our right to labor in it must be firmly established . . . How can we expect to be able to hold meetings much longer when people are so diligently taught to despise us for thus stepping out of the 'sphere of woman!' Look at this instance: after we had left Groton the Abolition minister there, at Lyceum meeting poured out his sarcasm and ridicule upon our heads and among other things said, he would as soon be caught robbing a hen roost as encouraging a woman to lecture . . . If we surrender the right to speak to the public this year, we must surrender the right to petition next year and the right to write the year after and so on. What then can woman do for the slave when she is herself under the feet of man and shamed into silence? . . .
>
> Anti Slavery men are trying very hard to separate what God hath joined together. I fully believe that . . . no such attempt can ever be successful. They blend with each other like the colors of the rainbow.
>
> —Angelina Grimké, abolitionist and women's rights advocate
> Letter to abolitionists Theodore Weld and John Greenleaf Whittier
> August 20, 1837

1. According to Angelina Grimké, what was expected of women at the time?

_____

_____

2. Why do you think Grimké began fighting for women's rights as well the rights of slaves?

_____

_____

_____

Activity 3

Document-Based Activity

The Second Great Awakening

Writing a Document-Based Essay

HISTORICAL CONTEXT In 1801 a series of large, outdoor, religious meetings were held in Kentucky. Mass revivals later spread through the other western states. In the 1820s and 1830s preachers such as Charles Finney promoted revivalism in western New York and other parts of the Northeast. The movement became known as the Second Great Awakening. Religious passion intensified. Church membership soared. The Awakening also helped spark an era of social reform. Americans moved by spiritual fervor became a force for cultural change in the mid-1800s.

TASK Using information from the documents and your knowledge of American history, write an essay in which you:

- Explain why so many people attended religious revivals in the early 1800s.

- Discuss how the Second Great Awakening inspired movements for social change in America.

Part B

DIRECTIONS Using the information from the documents provided and your knowledge of history, write a well-organized essay that includes an introduction, a body of several paragraphs, and a conclusion. In the body of the essay, use examples from at least *four* documents. Support your response with relevant facts, examples, and details. Include additional outside information.

GUIDELINES
In your essay, be sure to:

- Address all aspects of the **Task** by accurately analyzing and interpreting at least *four* documents.

- Incorporate information from the documents in the body of the essay.

- Incorporate relevant outside information.

- Support the theme with relevant facts, examples, and details.

- Use a logical and clear plan of organization.

- Introduce the theme by establishing a framework that is beyond a simple statement of the **Task** or **Historical Context**.

- Conclude the essay with a summation of the theme.

Activity 4   Document-Based Activity

African Americans and the Civil War

Using Source Materials

HISTORICAL CONTEXT When the Civil War began in 1861, African Americans were eager to join the fight. Not allowed to enlist as soldiers, black men and women helped the Union war effort by serving as laborers, teamsters, cooks, nurses, guides, and spies. By the fall of 1862 the North needed more troops. President Lincoln then authorized the creation of black regiments that would be commanded by white officers. Though they were paid less than whites and often given difficult assignments, African American soldiers fought with great skill and courage on the battlefield.

TASK Using information from the documents and your knowledge of American history, answer the questions that follow each document in Part A. Your answers to the questions will help you write the Part B essay.

Part A

DIRECTIONS Examine the following documents and answer the short-answer questions that follow each document.

DOCUMENT 1

> But the cry went forth—"We won't have the Negroes . . . we won't have them in the army, nor about us." Yet scarcely had you got into conflict with the South, when you were glad to receive the news that contrabands [escaped southern slaves] brought . . . They have tried to keep the Negro out of the war, but they could not keep him out, and now they drag him in, with his news, and are glad to do so. General Wool [a Union officer] says the contrabands have brought the most reliable news.
>
> —Speech by William Wells Brown, abolitionist and former slave
> American Anti-Slavery Society annual meeting, May 6, 1862, New York

1. How did northern whites first view African American participation in the Civil War?

_____

_____

2. Why did northerners quickly come to appreciate the contrabands?

_____

_____

Activity 4

Document-Based Activity

African Americans and the Civil War

DOCUMENT 2

Before You Read The following words in the document below may be new to you: *maw, insurgents, menial.* You may want to use a dictionary to look them up.

> But when the war trumpet sounded o'er the land, . . . the Black man laid his life at the altar of the nation,—and he was refused. When the arms of the Union were beaten, in the first year of the war, and the Executive called for more food for its ravenous maw, again the black man begged the privilege of aiding his country in her need, to be again refused.
>
> And now he is in the War, and how has he conducted himself? Let their dusky forms rise up, out of the mires of James Island [a battleground in South Carolina], and give the answer . . . Obedient and patient and solid as a wall are they. All we lack is a paler hue and a better acquaintance with the alphabet.
>
> Now your Excellency, we have done a Soldier's duty. Why can't we have a Soldier's pay? You caution the Rebel [Confederate] chieftain, that the United States knows no distinction in her soldiers. She insists on having all her soldiers of whatever creed or color, to be treated according to the usages of War. Now if the United States exacts uniformity of treatment of her soldiers from the insurgents, would it not be well and consistent to set the example herself by paying all her soldiers alike? . . .
>
> We appeal to you, Sir, as the Executive of the Nation, to have us justly dealt with. The Regt. [regiment] do pray that they be assured their service will be fairly appreciated by paying them as American Soldiers, not as menial hirelings. Black men, you may well know, are poor; three dollars per month, for a year, will supply their needy wives and little ones with fuel. If you . . . will assure us of our whole pay, we are content.
>
> —Corporal James Henry Gooding, 54th Massachusetts Infantry
> Letter to President Abraham Lincoln, September 28, 1863

1. Why did Corporal Gooding write this letter?

_____

_____

2. What arguments does Gooding use to make his case?

_____

_____

_____

　　　　　　　　　　Document-Based Activities

Document-Based Activity

African Americans and the Civil War

DOCUMENT 3

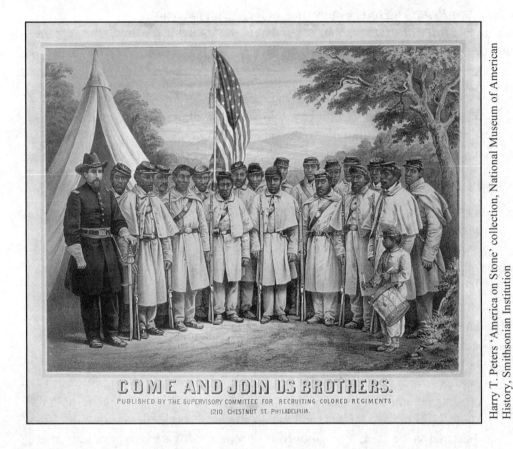

COME AND JOIN US BROTHERS.
PUBLISHED BY THE SUPERVISORY COMMITTEE FOR RECRUITING COLORED REGIMENTS
1210 CHESTNUT ST. PHILADELPHIA.

Harry T. Peters 'America on Stone' collection, National Museum of American History, Smithsonian Institution

1. What was the purpose of this poster? What feelings did it attempt to stir among African Americans?

_____

_____

_____

_____

2. By looking at this poster, what can you infer about conditions for African Americans in the U.S. Army in 1863?

_____

_____

_____

_____

Activity 4

Document-Based Activity

African Americans and the Civil War

DOCUMENT 4

Before You Read The following words in the document below may be new to you: *alleviate*, *adage*. You may want to use a dictionary to look them up.

About four o'clock, July 2, the charge was made. The firing could be plainly heard in camp. I hastened down to the landing and remained there until eight o'clock that morning. When the wounded arrived, or rather began to arrive, the first one brought in was Samuel Anderson of our company. He was badly wounded. Then others of our boys, some with their legs off, arm gone, foot off, and wounds of all kinds imaginable. They had to wade through creeks and marshes, as they were discovered by the enemy and shelled very badly. A number of the men were lost, some got fastened in the mud and had to cut off the legs of their pants, to free themselves. The 103d New York suffered the most, as their men were very badly wounded.

My work now began. I gave my assistance to try to alleviate their sufferings. I asked the doctor at the hospital what I could get for them to eat. They wanted soup, but that I could not get; but I had a few cans of condensed milk and some turtle eggs, so I thought I would try to make some custard. I had doubts as to my success, for cooking with turtle eggs was something new to me, but the adage has it, "Nothing ventured, nothing done," so I made a venture and the result was a very delicious custard. This I carried to the men, who enjoyed it very much. My services were given at all times for the comfort of these men. I was on hand to assist whenever needed. I was enrolled as company laundress, but I did very little of it, because I was always busy doing other things through camp, and was employed all the time doing something for the officers and comrades.

—Susie King Taylor, volunteer with the Union army
A Black Woman's Civil War Memoirs

1. What hardships for African American soldiers does Susie Taylor discuss in her letter?

_____

_____

_____

2. How did Taylor contribute to the Union war effort?

_____

_____

Document-Based Activities

Activity 4   # Document-Based Activity

African Americans and the Civil War

DOCUMENT 5

Before You Read The following words in the document below may be new to you: *furlough*, *provisions*. You may want to use a dictionary to look them up.

Our crew are principally colored; and a braver set of men never trod the deck of an American ship. We have been on several expeditions recently. On the 15th of April our ship and other gunboats proceeded up the Rappahannock River for some distance, and finding no rebel batteries to oppose us, we concluded to land the men from the different boats and make a raid. I was ordered by the Commodore to beat the call for all parties to go on shore. No sooner had I executed the order than every man was at his post, our own color being first to land. At first there was a little prejudice against our colored men going on shore, but it soon died away. We succeeded in capturing 3 fine horses, 6 cows, 5 hogs, 6 sheep, 3 calves, an abundance of chickens, 600 pounds of pork, 300 bushels of corn, and succeeded in liberating from the horrible pit of bondage 10 men, 6 women, and 8 children . . .

On the 28th of April we landed two boats' crew, armed and equipped, on the shore at Mathias Point, a distance of seventy-five miles from Washington, and captured 400 pounds of salt pork, corn, &c. [etc.], and a rebel captain, who happened to be home on a furlough eating his dinner . . .

On the 9th of May we landed three boats' crew on shore at night and captured a rebel signal company and . . . all their provisions . . .

On Thursday, the 12th . . . we were notified that wounded soldiers were drifting on rafts in the river near Aquia Creek, having been driven there by guerillas in their retreat from the front. We have been lying here ever since – when there have been over 20,000 wounded brought here to be transported to Washington.

—George W. Reed, drummer, U.S.S. *Commodore Reed*
Letter printed in the *Christian Recorder*, a black newspaper, May 21, 1864

1. What duties did George Reed perform on his ship?

_____

_____

2. The gunboat *Commodore Reed* engaged in what types of missions?

_____

_____

Activity 4

Document-Based Activity
African Americans and the Civil War

DOCUMENT 6

Before You Read The following words in the document below may be new to you: *impressed, feigned, skill, thence.* You may want to use a dictionary to look them up.

I was taken prisoner at the surrender of Athens, Alabama, September 20th, 1864. We were marched to Mobile, Alabama, stopping at various places on the route. We were twelve days going to Mobile. After we were captured, the rebels robbed us of everything we had that they could use; they searched our pockets, took our clothing, and even cut the buttons off what little clothing they allowed us to retain. After arriving at Mobile, we were placed at work on the fortifications there, and impressed colored men who were at work when we arrived were released, we taking their places. We were kept at hard labor and inhumanly treated; if we lagged or faltered, or misunderstood an order, we were whipped and abused; some of our own men being detailed to whip others. They gave as a reason for such harsh treatment, that we knew very well what they wanted us to do, but that we feigned ignorance; that if we were with the Yankees, we could do all they wanted, &c. [etc.]. For the slightest cause we were subjected to the lash. We were very poorly provided with food, our rations being corn-meal and mule-meat, and occasionally some poor beef. On the 7th of December, I stole a skiff and went down Mobile River to the Bay, and was taken on board of one of our Gun-boats. Was taken to Fort Morgan on the Gun-boat, and reported to the commanding officer, who, after hearing my story, furnished me with a pass and transportation to New Orleans; from there I was sent to Cairo, thence to Louisville, and from there here [Nashville].

—Private Joseph Howard, 44th U.S. Colored Infantry
Letter to his commanding officer, Major J. H. Cochrane, January 3, 1865

---

1. What happened to Private Howard after he was captured by the Confederates?

_____

_____

_____

2. Do you think white prisoners would have been treated differently? Explain.

_____

_____

_____

_____

Activity 4

Document-Based Activity

African Americans and the Civil War

DOCUMENT 7

Before You Read The following words in the document below may be new to you: *coveted, valor*. You may want to use a dictionary to look them up.

> Negro troops stood face to face with Forest's veteran cavalry [Confederate troops]. The fire was growing hotter, and balls were uncomfortably thick. At length, the enemy in strong force, with banners flying, bore down toward us in full sight, apparently bent on mischief. Pointing to the advancing column, I said, as I passed along the line, "Boys, it looks very much like fight; keep cool, do your duty." . . .
>
> Forest . . . after testing our line, and finding it unyielding, turned to the east, and struck over toward Murfreesboro . . .
>
> Soon after taking our position in line at Nashville, we were closely besieged by Hood's army . . . As soon as the fog lifted, the battle began in good earnest. Hood mistook my assault for an attack in force upon his right flank, and weakening his left in order to meet it, gave the coveted opportunity to Thomas [a Union general], who improved it by assailing Hood's left flank . . . and capturing a large number of prisoners.
>
> Thus the first day's fight wore away. It had been for us a severe but glorious day. Over three hundred of my command had fallen, but everywhere our army was successful . . . General Steadman congratulated us, saying his only fear had been that we might fight too hard. We had done all he desired, and more. Colored soldiers had again fought side by side with white troops; they had mingled together in the charge; they had supported each other; they had assisted each other from the field when wounded, and they lay side by side in death. The survivors rejoiced together over a hard fought field, won by a common valor.
>
> —Colonel Thomas J. Morgan, 14th U.S. Colored Infantry
> Account of battles in the Franklin-Nashville campaign, late 1864

1. How does Colonel Morgan seem to feel about the soldiers he commands? Why?

_____

_____

2. How might the troops in the 14th U.S. Colored Infantry have helped contribute to social change in America?

_____

_____

Document-Based Activities

Activity 4

Document-Based Activity

African Americans and the Civil War

Writing a Document-Based Essay

HISTORICAL CONTEXT When the Civil War began in 1861, African Americans were eager to join the fight. Not allowed to enlist as soldiers, black men and women helped the Union war effort by serving as laborers, teamsters, cooks, nurses, guides, and spies. By the fall of 1862, the North needed more troops. President Lincoln then authorized the creation of black regiments that would be commanded by white officers. Though they were paid less than whites and often given difficult assignments, African American soldiers fought with great skill and courage on the battlefield.

TASK Using information from the documents and your knowledge of American history, write an essay in which you:

- Discuss the role African Americans played in the Civil War.

- Explain the challenges African Americans faced while contributing to the Union war effort.

Part B

DIRECTIONS Using the information from the documents provided and your knowledge of American history, write a well-organized essay that includes an introduction, a body of several paragraphs, and a conclusion. In the body of the essay, use examples from at least *four* documents. Support your response with relevant facts, examples, and details. Include additional outside information.

GUIDELINES
In your essay, be sure to:

- Address all aspects of the **Task** by accurately analyzing and interpreting at least *four* documents.

- Incorporate information from the documents in the body of the essay.

- Incorporate relevant outside information.

- Support the theme with relevant facts, examples, and details.

- Use a logical and clear plan of organization.

- Introduce the theme by establishing a framework that is beyond a simple statement of the **Task** or **Historical Context**.

- Conclude the essay with a summation of the theme.

Activity 5

Document-Based Activity

Reconstruction

Using Source Materials

HISTORICAL CONTEXT Reconstruction was the process by which the southern states that had seceded were restored to the Union. As part of this process, Radical Republicans in the North wanted to establish social and political equality for southern blacks. Congress created the Freedmen's Bureau to help former slaves adjust to life as free citizens. Three Constitutional amendments and several federal laws granted equal rights to African Americans. Many white southerners, however, ignored the new laws and worked to preserve white rule in the South.

TASK Using information from the documents and your knowledge of American history, answer the questions that follow each document in Part A. Your answers to the questions will help you write the Part B essay.

Part A

DIRECTIONS Examine the following documents and answer the short-answer questions that follow each document.

DOCUMENT 1

> I asked what he thought of the extension of the franchise so as to make the Negro a voter. Like almost every other man with whom I have talked in this State, he was utterly opposed to it. The Negro was not fit to vote; it wasn't in his nature ever to become fit to vote; and the Southern people wouldn't stand it if the North should put the Negro and the white man on an equality. That would make the South fight . . . Let the Negro vote, and the Southern people will have to be kept down by a standing army.
>
> —John Richard Dennett, northern journalist who toured the South
> Account of a conversation with a white Virginian, July 1865

1. What did most Virginians think about African American suffrage?

_____

_____

2. Why do you think that many Virginians may have held these opinions?

_____

_____

Activity 5

Document-Based Activity

Reconstruction

DOCUMENT 2

Before You Read The following words in the document below may be new to you: *garrisoned, auger, spasmodic, body politic, miscegenation, amalgamation, odious, dogma, mongrel.* You may want to use a dictionary to look them up.

Our country is now in a disturbed condition caused by the fiery ordeal through which we just passed & the total absence of both military or civil law in all parts of this state except the few garrisoned towns. Were it not for the national quiet and law abiding disposition of our people we would be subjected to the auger of lawlessness and outrage . . .

By this sudden system of Emancipation, this spasmodic transformation of the ignorant Negro from a peaceful laborer who has been accustomed to have all needs . . . provided . . . both in sickness & health to a self reliant citizen will paralyze the productive resources of the South. It . . . can cause a famine in this our fertile land. If we could have a system of gradual emancipation & colonization our people would universally rejoice & be glad to get rid of slavery which has ever been a cancer upon the body politic of our social organization . . . We would gladly substitute white for slave labor but we can never regard the Negro our equal either intellectually or socially. The doctrine of "Miscegenation" or as the word which is a Latin compound ("Misco" to mix & "genus" race) signifies an amalgamation of the races, is odious, destructive & contrary to the laws of God & Man. If such a detestable dogma becomes a law we shall soon have a race of mulattoes as fickle & foolish as the Mongrel population of Mexico never content with their present condition but always desiring a change of government & rulers.

—Edwin H. McCaleb, former officer in the Confederate Army
Letter to a northern acquaintance, T. P. Chandler, June 1, 1865

---

1. How did McCaleb feel about slavery? How did he feel about African Americans?

_____

_____

2. What did McCaleb believe should happen in the South? What did he fear would happen?

_____

_____

_____

DOCUMENT 3

Before You Read The following words in the document below may be new to you: *vagabond*, *larcener*, *audacious*, *whisht*. You may want to use a dictionary to look them up.

Enough that Radicalism is a moral epidemic & like other epidemics must run its course. Any effort to resist its headlong tendencies now only add fuel to the flame. One thing, however, I hold that there is but one solution for the problem. *We* have to make the passage of the Red Sea. The negro emerging from the control of his master, becomes first a vagabond. His next step makes him a larcener. The progress is rapid from petty to audacious thieving, and his next advance is to felony. He becomes a burglar; commits arson, murder & highway robbery; and, soon thereafter, he bands with numbers, & begins the war of race, by plundering & burning towns & villages. Seven millions of whites will not rest long under the rule of 3 millions of negroes; or if they do, the natural question will be, as it has long been with me—"Is our race worth saving?" Brood over it; organize promptly in every precinct; get good weapons, establish places of rendezvous, provide signal & pass words; seek your places of rendezvous through the woods & not by the highways, & keep your powder dry. In the cities, every *square* should have its *whisht* club, consisting of the trusty whites of the square itself. These should send delegates to the general club of the city & country, in every country. In the event of alarm in the city, let each square club have a house of rendezvous within the square, and seek it, not by emerging into the streets, but by rear passages over fences &c. [etc.]. Individuals leaving their houses by the front will be very apt to be butchered. The members of the square club, emerging in numbers from 15 to 50, more or less constitute organized companies; & these uniting with the clubs of the ward, become regiments & brigades, equal to the danger.

—W. Gilmore Simms, southern novelist
Letter to a friend, John Esten Cooke, May 9, 1868

1. What threat did W. Gilmore Simms think freed slaves posed?

_____

_____

2. What course of action did Simms recommend for southern whites?

_____

_____

Activity 5

Document-Based Activity

Reconstruction

DOCUMENT 4

Before You Read The following words in the document below may be new to you: *desperadoes*, *rapine*. You may want to use a dictionary to look them up.

> The roaming bands of desperadoes who make the freedmen and northern men their particular objects of murder and rapine have done much to keep alive the dying embers of sectional ill feeling. The men who form these bands are chiefly the debris of the rebel army, who have not devoted themselves to any industrial pursuits for their maintenance since the close of the war.
>
> The difficulties in the way of the performance of the duties of the officers of the bureau are much increased by the existence of certain State statutes which affect the freed people alone, and which are unjust and oppressive. (See the statutes forbidding the freed people to carry arms; to lease or purchase land in the country; and the statute requiring them to contract for the year before the 10th day of January of each year, or obtain a license to do job work.) It is true that these statutes are nullified by the civil rights bill; but so long as the prejudices of the white people are protected and encouraged by formal statues of State legislation, it will be impossible to obtain a thorough enforcement of the provisions of the civil rights bill intended for the especial protection of the freed people . . .
>
> As before remarked, the prejudice existing on account of color is only in the lowest courts, and among the unthinking people. In the higher courts, generally, prejudice on account of color does not exist. The securing of justice to the freedmen can only be left to the courts now that military authority resumes its subordinate place in the affairs of the government.
>
> —Major General Thomas J. Wood
> Report to Congress about the Freedmen's Bureau in Mississippi
> October 31, 1866

1. How did the government of Mississippi discriminate against African Americans?

_____

_____

_____

2. According to Major Wood, what kinds of people undermined Reconstruction?

_____

_____

Activity 5

Document-Based Activity

Reconstruction

DOCUMENT 5
"Getting Out the Negro Vote," *Harper's Weekly*, 1868

Picture History

1. Who does the African American man in the illustration represent? Who do the men with guns represent?

_____

_____

_____

_____

_____

2. How would you summarize the principal message of this illustration?

_____

_____

_____

_____

_____

Activity 5

Document-Based Activity

Reconstruction

DOCUMENT 6

Before You Read The following words in the document below may be
new to you: *perpetrators*, *conjunction*. You may want to use a dictionary to
look them up.

At this time the hostility to colored schools was so great that many acts of
personal violence and insult were committed on the teachers, school-
houses were burned, and pupils beaten and frightened.

As the military force began to be withdrawn from the smaller places in
the country, schools had to be discontinued for want of protection, as the
civil authorities would do little or nothing to protect the freed people in the
enjoyment of their rights, or punish the perpetrators of outrage where the
injured party was a negro. Planters refused to board teachers, and so
teachers had to abandon their schools or occupy rooms and board with the
colored people. This state of things, taken in conjunction with the heavy
debt contracted previously on account of the school department, (more than
$80,000,) made it look exceedingly gloomy for the future of the colored
schools in the State of Louisiana . . .

In the city of New Orleans, during the month of August, four colored
churches, also used for school purposes, were burned, and attempts made
to fire several other buildings used as school-houses. One church nearly
finished, at a cost of about $1,000, was completely demolished in one
night, because a colored school was to have been opened in it the next
week. Through fear the children dared not attend, and thus many schools
which were about to be opened had to be given up.

— Major General Philip H. Sheridan
Report to Congress about the Freedmen's Bureau in Louisiana
October 31, 1866

---

1. How did some people in Louisiana try to block the establishment of schools for
African Americans?

_____

_____

2. Besides some people's hostility, what obstacles stood in the way of black schools?

_____

_____

_____

Document-Based Activity

Reconstruction

DOCUMENT 7

Before You Read The following words in the document below may be
new to you: *subverted, redress*. You may want to use a dictionary to look
them up.

> We would respectfully state that life, liberty and property are unprotected
> among the colored race of this state. Organized Bands of desperate and
> lawless men mainly composed of soldiers of the late Rebel Armies Armed
> disciplined and disguised and bound by Oath and secret obligations have
> by force terror and violence subverted all civil society among Colored
> people, thus utterly rendering insecure the safety of persons and property,
> overthrowing all those rights which are the primary basis and objects of the
> Government which are expressly guaranteed to us by the Constitution of
> the United States as amended; We believe you are not familiar with the
> description of the Ku Klux Klans riding nightly over the country going
> from County to County and . . . spreading terror wherever they go, by
> robbing whipping ravishing and killing our people without provocation . . .
>
> The Legislature has adjourned they refused to enact any laws to suppress
> Ku Klux disorder. We regard them as now being licensed to continue their
> dark and bloody deeds under cover of the dark night. They refuse to allow
> us to testify in the state Courts where a white man is concerned . . . We
> also find that for our services to the Government and our race we have
> become the special object of hatred and persecution at the hands of the
> Democratic party. Our people are driven from their homes in great
> numbers having no redress only the U.S. Courts which is in many cases
> unable to reach them. We would state that we have been law abiding
> citizens, pay our tax and in many parts of the state our people have been
> driven from the poles, refused the right to vote. Many have been
> slaughtered while attempting to vote, we ask how long is this state of
> things to last.
>
> —Committee of African American citizens from Frankfort, Kentucky
> Petition to Congress, March 25, 1871

1. Why are the authors of this petition critical of the government of Kentucky?

_____

_____

2. Why do you think the authors wrote this petition?

_____

_____

Activity 5 # Document-Based Activity

Reconstruction

Writing a Document-Based Essay

HISTORICAL CONTEXT Reconstruction was the process by which the southern states that had seceded were restored to the Union. As part of this process, Radical Republicans in the North wanted to establish social and political equality for southern blacks. Congress created the Freedmen's Bureau to help former slaves adjust to life as free citizens. Three Constitutional amendments and several federal laws granted equal rights to African Americans. Many white southerners, however, ignored the new laws and worked to preserve white rule in the South.

TASK Using information from the documents and your knowledge of American history, write an essay in which you:

- Explain why so many white southerners were strongly opposed to Reconstruction.

- Describe how white people in the South resisted the federal government's attempts to establish social and political equality for African Americans.

Part B

DIRECTIONS Using the information from the documents provided and your knowledge of American history, write a well-organized essay that includes an introduction, a body of several paragraphs, and a conclusion. In the body of the essay, use examples from at least *four* documents. Support your response with relevant facts, examples, and details. Include additional outside information.

GUIDELINES
In your essay, be sure to:

- Address all aspects of the **Task** by accurately analyzing and interpreting at least *four* documents.

- Incorporate information from the documents in the body of the essay.

- Incorporate relevant outside information.

- Support the theme with relevant facts, examples, and details.

- Use a logical and clear plan of organization.

- Introduce the theme by establishing a framework that is beyond a simple statement of the **Task** or **Historical Context**.

- Conclude the essay with a summation of the theme.

Activity 6   Document-Based Activity

The Second Industrial Revolution

Using Source Materials

HISTORICAL CONTEXT In the late 1800s industrialization transformed
the American economy. Steam-powered machines increased the pace of
production. Mass-produced goods rolled out of factories. The industrialists
who owned these plants amassed great fortunes. Industrialization, however,
created many hardships for the workers. They toiled long hours in factories
and mines for low wages. Labor leaders organized unions to try to improve
the workers' situation. Industrial capitalists resisted their efforts, increasing
the unrest among the laboring classes.

TASK Using information from the documents and your knowledge of
American history, answer the questions that follow each document in
Part A. Your answers to the questions will help you write the Part B essay.

Part A

DIRECTIONS Examine the following documents and answer the short-
answer questions that follow each document.

DOCUMENT 1

> If workingmen and capitalists are equal co-partners, composing one vast
> firm by which the industry of the world is carried on and controlled, why
> do they not share equally in the profits? Why does capital take to itself the
> whole loaf, while labor is left to gather up the crumbs? Why does capital
> roll in luxury and wealth, while labor is left to eke out a miserable
> existence in poverty and want? Are these the evidences . . . of equal
> partnership? No, sir. On the contrary, they are evidences of an antagonism.
>
> —William H. Sylvis, president of the iron molders' union
> Speech in Buffalo, New York, 1864

1. How does William Sylvis view the industrial capitalists of his day?

_____

_____

2. Why do you think Sylvis gave this speech?

_____

_____

Activity 6

Document-Based Activity

The Second Industrial Revolution

DOCUMENT 2

Strikes were occurring almost every hour . . . Up to the 22nd, no trouble had occurred at Reading. There were some men on a strike, and trains had been stopped, but the crowds that gathered about the stations, were citizens drawn to those places to satisfy an idle curiosity . . .

At ten minutes after eight o'clock the military marched in toward Penn street, through the cut, from the depot. They were about three hundred and fifty strong, and they marched, to the tap of a few drums that could not be heard a square away. Few people were aware of their arrival . . . when suddenly three hundred rifles were discharged in volleys, and five men dropped to the pavements . . . The troops continued their firing, and men, women and children fled in fear . . .

The presence of the military did not curb the spirit of the rioters. On the contrary they grew bolder and more threatening. For some days after the fight open attacks on the trains were made.

The strikers mounted a passing loaded coal train, put on the brakes, stopped the train and pushed back the caboose and several loaded cars, thus virtually blockading the down track. One of the eight-ton cars was dumped on the rails . . . The freight up from Philadelphia and the market train were compelled to halt and go no further. At this point the passenger train down, was stopped in the cut, where the fighting took place. The crew was compelled to desert and the passengers were obliged to leave . . .

At a quarter after eleven o'clock, the night of the 25th, the strikers had torn down the watch boxes at the street corners, and proceeded down the road to tear up the tracks. They signalled their departure by a perfect hurricane of yells and cheering, as they proceeded in their onward march of ruin and destruction . . . The cry among the men was, "Wages and revenge."

—Joseph A. Dacus, editor of the *St. Louis Republican*
Account of the railroad workers' strike in Reading, Pennsylvania, 1877

1. How and why did the Reading strikers change their tactics?

_____

_____

2. Was the military response to the strike effective? Explain.

_____

_____

Document-Based Activities

Activity 6

Document-Based Activity

The Second Industrial Revolution

DOCUMENT 3

Before You Read The following word in the document below may be new to you: *emoluments*. You may want to use a dictionary to look it up.

If we desire to enjoy the blessings of life . . . a check should be placed upon . . . unjust accumulation, and a system adopted which will secure to the laborer the fruits of his toil; and as this much desired object can only be accomplished by the thorough unification of labor, and the united effort of those who obey the divine injunction that "In the sweat of thy brow shalt thou eat bread," we have formed the * * * * * [Knights of Labor] with a view of securing the organization and direction, by co-operative effort, of the power of the industrial classes; and we submit to the world the object sought to be accomplished by our organization, calling upon all who believe in securing "the greatest good to the greatest number" to aid and assist us:—

I. To bring within the folds of organization every department of productive industry, making knowledge a standpoint for action . . .

II. To secure to the toilers a proper share of the wealth that they create; more of the leisure that rightfully belongs to them; . . . more of the benefits, privileges, and emoluments of the world . . .

XI. The prohibition of the employment of children in workshops, mines, and factories before attaining their fourteenth year . . .

XIII. To secure for both sexes equal pay for equal work . . .

XIV. The reduction of the hours of labor to eight per day, so that the laborers may have more time for social enjoyment and intellectual improvement, and be enabled to reap the advantages conferred by the labor-saving machinery which their brains have created.

—Preamble to the Knights of Labor Constitution, 1878

1. According to this excerpt, what specific improvements in working conditions did the Knights of Labor seek?

_____

_____

_____

2. What did the Knights believe was necessary for them to achieve their goals?

_____

_____

Activity 6

Document-Based Activity
The Second Industrial Revolution

DOCUMENT 4
Puck, August 15, 1883

1. Who does the man tied to the stake represent? What groups are depicted as his fire-breathing tormentors? (Hint: The name "Depew" labels one of the flames spewing forth from one of the log's mouths. It refers to Chauncey Depew, a politician and vice president of the New York Central Railroad.)

_____

_____

2. How would you express the primary message of this cartoon?

_____

_____

Activity 6

Document-Based Activity

The Second Industrial Revolution

DOCUMENT 5

Before You Read The following words in the document below may be
new to you: *Bohemians, contiguous.* You may want to use a dictionary to
look them up.

Probably more than half of all the Bohemians in this city [New York] are
cigarmakers, and it is the herding of these in great numbers in the so-called
tenement factories, where the cheapest grade of work is done at the lowest
wages, that constitutes at once their greatest hardship and the chief grudge
of other workmen against them. The manufacturer who owns, say, from
three or four to a dozen or more tenements contiguous to his shop, fills
them up with these people, charging them outrageous rents, and . . . deals
them out tobacco by the week, and devotes the rest of his energies to the
paring down of wages to within a peg or two of the point where the tenant
rebels in desperation. When he does rebel, he is given the alternative of
submission, or eviction with entire loss of employment . . .

Take a row of houses in East Tenth Street as an instance. They contained
thirty-five families of cigarmakers, with probably not half a dozen persons
in the whole lot of them, outside of the children, who could speak a word
of English, though many had been in the country half a lifetime. This room
with two windows giving on the street, and a rear attachment without
windows, called a bedroom by courtesy, is rented at $12.25 a month. In the
front room man and wife work at the bench from six in the morning till
nine at night. They make a team, stripping the tobacco leaves together;
then he makes the filler, and she rolls the wrapper on and finishes the cigar.
For a thousand they receive $3.75, and can turn out together three thousand
cigars a week . . . The workers in these tenements are just now on a strike,
demanding $5.00 and $5.50 for their work . . . While we are in the house,
the ultimatum of the "boss" is received. He will give $3.75 a thousand, not
another cent.

—Jacob Riis, photojournalist
How the Other Half Lives, 1890

1. What hardships did the cigar makers face?

_____

_____

2. Why did the workers have little power to improve their situation?

_____

_____

Activity 6

Document-Based Activity

The Second Industrial Revolution

DOCUMENT 6

Before You Read The following term in the document below may be new to you: *body politic*. You may want to use a dictionary to look it up.

Five reductions in wages, in work, and in conditions of employment swept through the shops at Pullman between May and December, 1893. The last was the most severe, amounting to nearly thirty per cent, and our rents had not fallen. We owed Pullman $70,000 when we struck May 11. We owe him twice as much today. He does not evict us for two reasons: One, the force of popular sentiment and public opinion; the other because he hopes to starve us out, to break through in the back of the American Railway Union, and to deduct from our miserable wages when we are forced to return to him the last dollar we owe him for the occupancy of his houses.

Rents all over the city in every quarter of its vast extent have fallen, in some cases to one-half. Residences, compared with which ours are hovels, can be had a few miles away at the price we have been contributing to make a millionaire a billionaire. What we pay $15 for in Pullman is leased for $8 in Roseland . . .

Pullman . . . is an ulcer on the body politic. He owns the houses, the schoolhouses, and churches of God in the town he gave his once humble name. The revenue he derives from these, the wages he pays out with one hand—the Pullman Palace Car Company, he takes back with the other—the Pullman Land Association. He is able by this to bid under any contract car shop in this country. His competitors in business, to meet this, must reduce the wages of their men. This gives him the excuse to reduce ours to conform to the market. His business rivals must in turn scale down; so must he. And thus the merry war—the dance of skeletons bathed in human tears—goes on, and it will go on, brothers, forever, unless you, the American Railway Union, stop it; end it; crush it out.

—Pullman Palace Car Company workers
Statement to the American Railway Union, 1894

1. What grievances did the Pullman workers have against George M. Pullman?

_____

_____

2. What did the writers of this statement hope to accomplish?

_____

_____

Document-Based Activities

Activity 6

Document-Based Activity

The Second Industrial Revolution

DOCUMENT 7

Before You Read The following words in the document below may be
new to you: *injunction, inducing, demoralization*. You may want to use a
dictionary to look them up.

> I was served with a very sweeping injunction that restrained me, as
> president of the union, from sending out any telegram or any letter or
> issuing any order that would have the effect of inducing or persuading men
> to withdraw from the service of the [Pullman] company, or that would in
> any manner whatsoever, according to the language of the injunction,
> interfere with the [railroads'] operation . . . That injunction was served
> simultaneously, or practically so, by all of the courts embracing or having
> jurisdiction in the territory in which the trouble existed. From Michigan to
> California there seemed to be concerted action on the part of the courts in
> restraining us from exercising any of the functions of our offices. That
> resulted practically in the demoralization of our ranks . . .
>
> As soon as the employees found that we were arrested [for violating the
> injunction] and taken from the scene of action, they became demoralized,
> and that ended the strike. It was not the soldiers that ended the strike; it
> was not the old brotherhoods that ended the strike; it was simply the United
> States courts that ended the strike. Our men were in a position that never
> would have been shaken under any circumstances if we had been permitted
> to remain upon the field; remain among them . . . The headquarters were
> demoralized and abandoned, and we could not answer any telegrams or
> questions that would come in . . . The men went back to work, and the
> ranks were broken, and the strike was broken up . . . not by the Army, and
> not by any other power, but simply and solely by the action of the United
> States courts in restraining us from discharging our duties as officers and
> representatives of the employees.
>
> —Eugene V. Debs, president of the American Railway Union
> Testimony to a House committee investigating the Pullman strike, 1894

1. Which side did the U.S. government support in the Pullman strike? What actions did
   the government take?

   _____

   _____

2. According to Eugene V. Debs, what effects did government intervention have?

   _____

   _____

Activity 6

Document-Based Activity
The Second Industrial Revolution

Writing a Document-Based Essay

HISTORICAL CONTEXT In the late 1800s industrialization transformed the American economy. Steam-powered machines increased the pace of production. Mass-produced goods rolled out of factories. The industrialists who owned these plants amassed great fortunes. Industrialization, however, created many hardships for the workers. They toiled long hours in factories and mines for low wages. Labor leaders organized unions to try to improve the workers' situation. Industrial capitalists resisted their efforts, increasing the unrest among the laboring classes.

TASK Using information from the documents and your knowledge of American history, write an essay in which you:

- Explain the goals of the labor movement in the late 1800s.

- Describe the barriers to achieving these goals that the workers at that time faced.

Part B

DIRECTIONS Using the information from the documents provided and your knowledge of American history, write a well-organized essay that includes an introduction, a body of several paragraphs, and a conclusion. In the body of the essay, use examples from at least *four* documents. Support your response with relevant facts, examples, and details. Include additional outside information.

GUIDELINES
In your essay, be sure to:

- Address all aspects of the **Task** by accurately analyzing and interpreting at least *four* documents.

- Incorporate information from the documents in the body of the essay.

- Incorporate relevant outside information.

- Support the theme with relevant facts, examples, and details.

- Use a logical and clear plan of organization.

- Introduce the theme by establishing a framework that is beyond a simple statement of the **Task** or **Historical Context**.

- Conclude the essay with a summation of the theme.

Activity 7

Document-Based Activity

The Women's Suffrage Movement

Using Source Materials

HISTORICAL CONTEXT At the turn of the twentieth century, the struggle for women's suffrage was spearheaded by the National American Woman Suffrage Association (NAWSA). By 1913 women could vote in nine states. Some suffragists, however, wanted faster results. Led by Alice Paul, they formed the more militant National Woman's Party (NWP), which organized marches, pickets, and other protests to advance the cause. In the late 1910s the NAWSA and the NWP together waged a successful campaign for a women's suffrage amendment to the Constitution.

TASK Using information from the documents and your knowledge of American history, answer the questions that follow each document in Part A. Your answers to the questions will help you write the Part B essay.

Part A

DIRECTIONS Examine the following documents and answer the short-answer questions that follow each document.

DOCUMENT 1

> Here is a letter just sent up by a New Orleans woman: "We are afraid, if we come into your Association, that colored clubs may some day be let in, and that we shall find ourselves obliged to meet colored women on a footing of equality." I think I have heard that the South believes in State rights. The National American W. S. A. recognizes them. Louisiana has the right to regulate the conditions of membership for Louisiana . . . It is perfectly safe for you to come in on that basis.
>
> —Carrie Chapman Catt, NAWSA president
> Speech at the NAWSA convention, New Orleans, 1903

1. Why was the woman from New Orleans reluctant to join the NAWSA?

_____

_____

2. What was Carrie Chapman Catt's position regarding race and the NAWSA?

_____

_____

Activity 7

Document-Based Activity
The Women's Suffrage Movement

DOCUMENT 2

Before You Read The following words in the document below may be new to you: *implacably*, *polyglot*. You may want to use a dictionary to look them up.

> Some very active work has been carried on this summer in the Third Assembly District of the Borough of Manhattan by the Woman Suffrage Party . . . Beginning at St. Mark's Place we have moved south through the district until last Tuesday we held a stirring meeting near the southern boundary of the district, which is at the corner of Mott and Pell streets. This includes rough sections of the city, and Chinatown is one of the roughest. Many good friends warned us against going there, but our party, which aims to reach every section, sternly disallowed that any street, by-way, court or alley shall be closed to us. We suffragists are implacably against restricted districts of any kind . . . We expected a polyglot and varied crowd at the meeting at Mott and Pell streets. We took with us literature in Yiddish, Italian, and notices were written in Chinese. We were sure the politicians from the surrounding district political clubs would come out. We knew that many voters would be there whom we could reach, . . . that many a white-faced despairing woman could hear our message, that many struggling mothers and children would listen to us, that many of the respectable merchants and business men, both American and Chinese, who want better conditions, would welcome us, and that some of the social workers of the district would co-operate—to make our meeting successful. But we were not prepared to see the great orderly throng that greeted us. Many efficient police officers were stationed about, and any slight disturbances were immediately quelled.
>
> —Harriet Burton Laidlaw, suffragist
> *The Woman's Journal*, July 13, 1912

1. Why did some people advise against holding a meeting at the corner of Mott and Pell streets? Why did the suffragists proceed anyway?

_____

_____

_____

2. What was the outcome of the meeting?

_____

_____

Activity 7

Document-Based Activity

The Women's Suffrage Movement

DOCUMENT 3
Suffrage parade, Washington, D.C., March 3, 1913

Library of Congress Prints and Photographs Division

1. Do you think the suffragists chose a good location for their parade? Why or why not?

_____

_____

_____

2. Why might the woman at the left be carrying an American flag?

_____

_____

Activity 7

Document-Based Activity
The Women's Suffrage Movement

DOCUMENT 4

Before You Read The following words in the document below may be new to you: *efficacious, latent, dodgers*. You may want to use a dictionary to look them up.

> The moving picture houses, in particular, have been made the means of winning converts. Upon thousands of screens have been thrown the slogans of the Woman's Party calling upon the women voters to vote against [President Woodrow] Wilson because "he kept us out of suffrage."
>
> Billboarding and banners across the street have also been used lavishly by the Woman's Party throughout the suffrage states. In Kansas, Illinois, Arizona and Colorado particular emphasis has been placed upon this method of appeal.
>
> Perhaps none of the various campaign devices used by the Woman's Party has attracted more attention and been more efficacious in arousing the latent wrath of the Democrats than the street banners with their . . . call to the women voters to "vote against Wilson.". . .
>
> Another important phase of the Woman's Party activities which in its results is proving most effective in winning votes away from Wilson is the literature campaign. Leaflets and folders, appeals, cartoons and dodgers of various sorts have been distributed broadcast in an effort to reach the voting women. Many of them live on ranches or in rural districts where it has not been possible for speakers to reach them personally. In these cases literature has taken the place of speakers.
>
> A comprehensive text book has been prepared by Miss Lucy Burns, giving a complete survey of the record of the Democratic party on national suffrage and reasons why women should not vote to return that party to power. This was sent, early in the campaign, to the editors throughout all the suffrage states.
>
> —*The Suffragist*, October 21, 1916
> Report on the campaign activities of the National Woman's Party

1. Whom did the suffragists campaign against? Why?

_____

_____

2. What tactics did the National Woman's Party use to communicate its message?

_____

_____

Activity 7

Document-Based Activity
The Women's Suffrage Movement

DOCUMENT 5

Before You Read The following word in the document below may be new
to you: *pusillanimous*. You may want to use a dictionary to look it up.

We *can* get the Amendment through, and ratified . . . There should be a
mobilization of at least thirty-six state armies, and these armies should
move under the direction of the national officers . . . This great army with
its thirty-six, and let us hope, forty-eight divisions, should move on
Congress with precision, and a will . . . More, those who enter on this task,
should go prepared to give their lives and fortunes for success, and any
pusillanimous coward among us who dares to call retreat, should be
courtmartialled . . .

    We should win, if it is possible to do so, a few more states before the
Federal Amendment gets up to the legislatures . . . A southern state should
be selected and made ready for a campaign, and the solid front of the "anti"
south broken as soon as possible.

    Some break in the solid "anti" East should be made too. If New York
wins in 1917 the backbone of the opposition will be largely bent if not
broken . . .

    By 1920, when the next national party platforms will be adopted, we
should have won Iowa, South Dakota, North Dakota, Nebraska, New York,
Maine and a southern state. We should have secured the Illinois law in a
number of other states.

    With these victories to our credit and the tremendous increase in
momentum given the whole movement, we should be able to secure planks
in all platforms favoring the Federal Amendment (if it has not passed
before that time) and to secure its passage in the December term of the
1920 Congress.

—Carrie Chapman Catt
"Winning Plan" idea presented at the NAWSA convention, 1916

1. What was Carrie Chapman Catt's ultimate goal? How did she expect to achieve it?

_____

_____

2. Why do you think Catt used military imagery to outline her strategy?

_____

_____

Activity 7

Document-Based Activity

The Women's Suffrage Movement

DOCUMENT 6

Whereas, This country is now engaged in the greatest war in history [World War I], and

Whereas, The advocates of the Federal Amendment, though urging it as a war measure, announce, through their president, Mrs. Catt, that its passage "means a simultaneous campaign in 48 States. It demands organization in every precinct; activity, agitation, education in every corner. Nothing less than this nation-wide, vigilant, unceasing campaign will win the ratification," therefore be it

Resolved, That our country in this hour of peril should be spared the harassing of its public men and the distracting of its people from work for the war, and further

Resolved, That the United States Senate be respectfully urged to pass no measure involving such a radical change in our government while the attention of the patriotic portion of the American people is concentrated on the all-important task of winning the war, and during the absence of over a million men abroad.

—Women Voters Anti-Suffrage Party of New York
Petition to the U.S. Senate, 1917

1. Why did the signers of this petition oppose the suffrage campaign?

_____

_____

_____

_____

2. The petitioners note that supporters of the proposed amendment urged its passage "as a war measure." How might they have made the argument that women's suffrage was necessary because of the war?

_____

_____

_____

_____

Activity 7   Document-Based Activity
                            The Women's Suffrage Movement

DOCUMENT 7

Before You Read The following word in the second document below may
be new to you: *psychopathic*. You may want to use a dictionary to look
it up.

It does not seem right to treat American women who have petitioned for
the suffrage in the manner in which the women militants who have been
released from Occoquan jail [in Virginia] have been treated . . .

Mrs. Brannan describes the scene that took place in the reception room
on Nov. 14, following the arrests . . . "The guards fell upon us. I saw Miss
Lincoln, a slight young girl, thrown to the floor. Mrs. Nolan, a delicate old
lady of 73, was mastered by two men. The furniture was overturned and
the room was a scene of havoc. The whole group of women were thrown,
dragged and hurled out of the office . . . I was thrown, with four others, in a
cell with a narrow bed and dirty blankets."

—Lawrence, Massachusetts, *Telegram*, December 3, 1917

Alice Paul is in the psychopathic ward. She dreaded forcible feeding
frightfully, and I hate to think how she must be feeling. I had a nervous
time of it, gasping a long time afterward, and my stomach rejecting during
the process . . . I heard myself making the most hideous sounds, like an
animal in pain . . . One feels so forsaken when one lies prone and people
shove a pipe down one's stomach . . .

All the officers here know we are making this hunger strike that women
fighting for liberty may be considered political prisoners; we have told
them. God knows we don't want other women ever to have to do this over
again.

—"The Prison Notes of Rose Winslow"
The Suffragist, December 1, 1917

---

1. How did law enforcement officers treat women who picketed for suffrage?

_____

_____

2. What impact do you think the above articles had on the women's suffrage
   movement? Explain.

_____

_____

Activity 7   Document-Based Activity

The Women's Suffrage Movement

Writing a Document-Based Essay

HISTORICAL CONTEXT At the turn of the twentieth century, the struggle for women's suffrage was spearheaded by the National American Woman Suffrage Association (NAWSA). By 1913 women could vote in nine states. Some suffragists, however, wanted faster results. Led by Alice Paul, they formed the more militant National Woman's Party (NWP), which organized marches, pickets, and other protests to advance the cause. In the late 1910s the NAWSA and the NWP together waged a successful campaign for a women's suffrage amendment to the Constitution.

TASK Using information from the documents and your knowledge of American history, write an essay in which you:

- Discuss the strategies used by the leaders of the women's suffrage movement in the early 1900s.

- Explain the challenges facing the suffrage movement at this time.

Part B

DIRECTIONS Using the information from the documents provided and your knowledge of American history, write a well-organized essay that includes an introduction, a body of several paragraphs, and a conclusion. In the body of the essay, use examples from at least *four* documents. Support your response with relevant facts, examples, and details. Include additional outside information.

GUIDELINES
In your essay, be sure to:

- Address all aspects of the **Task** by accurately analyzing and interpreting at least *four* documents.

- Incorporate information from the documents in the body of the essay.

- Incorporate relevant outside information.

- Support the theme with relevant facts, examples, and details.

- Use a logical and clear plan of organization.

- Introduce the theme by establishing a framework that is beyond a simple statement of the **Task** or **Historical Context**.

- Conclude the essay with a summation of the theme.

Activity 8

Document-Based Activity

The First World War

Using Source Materials

HISTORICAL CONTEXT When World War I began in Europe in August 1914, the United States declared its neutrality. In practice, however, American trade policies favored the Allied nations. U.S. commerce with Britain and France tripled, while trade with Germany nearly disappeared. In January 1917 Germany started targeting all merchant ships destined for Britain. After German submarines sank several American vessels, the United States declared war on Germany in April 1917. A year and a half later the Allies finally defeated the Central Powers.

TASK Using information from the documents and your knowledge of American history, answer the questions that follow each document in Part A. Your answers to the questions will help you write the Part B essay.

Part A

DIRECTIONS Examine the following documents and answer the short-answer questions that follow each document.

DOCUMENT 1

> During the course of the war, the Allies were able to borrow $10.5 billion from sources in the United States, and $3.5 billion of that sum was raised before the United States actually entered the war . . . American manufacturers made war materials to Allied specifications and shipped them to the Allies . . . In this and in many other ways, the Allied armies of 1915 and 1916 were as heavily dependent on American industrial products as the Allied governments were on American cash.
>
> —John Mosier, military historian
> *The Myth of the Great War*

1. How did American civilians play a role in the Allied war effort?

_____

_____

2. What does this document reveal about America's stance on the war before 1917?

_____

_____

Activity 8   Document-Based Activity

The First World War

DOCUMENT 2

Before You Read The following words in the document below may be
new to you: *disposition*, *grandeur*. You may want to use a dictionary to
look them up.

FRENCH OFFICERS SHOULD TAKE INTO CONSIDERATION THE
IMPORTANCE OF THE MILITARY EFFORT MADE BY THE
UNITED STATES.

In April of 1917, at the moment of their entrance into the war, the
United States did not have, properly speaking, an army.

Within a year they have adopted universal and obligatory military
service, raised, armed, equipped, and sent to France several hundred
thousand men, and all of this is only the beginning. They have thus
accomplished a task of military organization without precedent in history.
They have accomplished and are now accomplishing within the interior of
France various works of enormous importance (improvements of the ports
of St. Nazaire and Bordeaux, storehouses and ice plants at Gièvres, etc.),
which will remain after the war and will enable us to undertake the
economic struggle under exceptionally favorable conditions as to
equipment.

The American Red Cross is placing at our disposition considerable
sums, to relieve people who have met with all kinds of misfortunes.

The General, Commander-in-Chief, desires that during their
conversations with American officers the French officers prove to the
American that the French fully appreciate the importance of the effort
furnished by America and the grandeur of the service rendered to France.

—General Henri Pétain, commander of the French armies
Letter of instruction to French liaison officers, May 8, 1918

---

1. What military and non-military assistance did Americans provide to France?

_____

_____

_____

2. How did General Henri Pétain feel about America's role in the war?

_____

_____

_____

Activity 8   Document-Based Activity

DOCUMENT 3
St. Nazaire, France, June 28, 1917

© CORBIS

1. This photograph of American ships arriving in France was taken about three months after the United States formally entered the war. What are these ships carrying?

_____

_____

2. If this photo had appeared in newspapers at the time, how do you think people in the Allied countries, the Central Powers, and the United States would have reacted?

_____

_____

_____

_____

_____

Document-Based Activities

Document-Based Activity

The First World War

DOCUMENT 4

I have just returned from a thorough inspection of the Services of Supply, having spent a day at each of the western ports of France and visited all of the principle depots, remount stations and hospitals . . . The results are especially gratifying in view of the handicap of the shortage of labor and material that has existed since April on account of tonnage being devoted to transportation of combatant troops to the exclusion of S.O.S. [Services of Supply] troops. I am satisfied now that we have builded properly and that there is no question whatever that the ports and our Services of Supply will be able to provide for the needs of our extended program.

. . . Right now there is a capacity approximating 25,000 tons per day at all our ports including Marseille and this will continue to increase . . . with our needs. Port efficiency will increase with experience and additional men and equipment.

. . . With the increased personnel and material called for, the rail facilities will be adequate. There need be no worry as to our ability to handle supplies as fast as our expanding tonnage will require. Even with scant labor supply, we have repaired about 13,000 French cars and a proportionate number of engines.

. . . Notwithstanding the scattered units of the command, supply trains have never failed to reach our troops, who have never been short of food for a day . . .

The work of engineers in construction is now only a matter of men and material, both of which are in sight . . . The great warehouses at Gièvres, Châteauroux, Méhun, and Is-sur-Tille are well advanced and will prove adequate for all requirements.

—John J. Pershing, commander of the American Expeditionary Force
Cable to Secretary of War Newton D. Baker, August 7, 1918

1. The Services of Supply was responsible for obtaining, storing, and distributing supplies for American forces. What challenges did it encounter in France?

_____

_____

_____

2. In this cable, how did John Pershing assess the capabilities of the Services of Supply?

_____

_____

Activity 8

Document-Based Activity

The First World War

DOCUMENT 5

Before You Read The following words in the document below may be
new to you: *requisitioned, droves, doughboy, laggards, aviators*. You may
want to use a dictionary to look them up.

The zero hour was 1:05 a.m., the heavy artillery starting it off . . . For four
hours the deafening roar continued as our messengers of death were hurled
into enemy territory. Then at 5:00 our infantry preceded by tanks went over
the top, making a picture of dash and activity.

Not content with ordinary progress the boys of our division leaped ahead
of the clumsy tanks and pressed forward in irresistible waves to the
German trenches.

The enemy artillery reply was feeble, though the infantry machine-gun
and rifle fire was more menacing.

Our artillery fire in the first place demoralized enemy resistance, and the
Boche [Germans] are surrendering in droves. Surely they must regret
giving up these luxurious dugouts and trenches which they have lived in
for four years. Many of them even have electric lights and good furniture
"requisitioned" from nearby French villages.

We must have slipped up on the enemy because they left a great deal of
equipment, ammunition and food . . . Up here in the advance we pass
prisoners in droves of from ten to a hundred with a doughboy in the rear
prodding the laggards with a bayonet whenever necessary . . .

The doughboys are still advancing swiftly. In the air we are supreme.
We are not in the position of the rat in the cage, as we were at Chateau-
Thierry when enemy planes swooped down upon us and threw streams of
machine-gun bullets into our ranks. This time the tables are turned. We see
our aviators flying over the retreating enemy, dropping bombs and creating
havoc.

—Corporal Elmer Sherwood, American Expeditionary Force
Journal entry, September 12, 1918, St. Mihiel, France

1. What was the sequence of events in the American offensive on St. Mihiel?

_____

_____

2. How did this victory represent significant progress for the Allies?

_____

_____

Activity 8

Document-Based Activity

The First World War

DOCUMENT 6

Before You Read The following words in the document below may be new to you: *salient, adversary, formidable.* You may want to use a dictionary to look them up.

> The reduction of the St. Mihiel salient completed the first task of the American Army. Its elimination freed . . . rail communications and the roads that paralleled the Meuse [River] north from St. Mihiel. These at once became available for our use in the greater offensive to be undertaken immediately. We had restored to France 200 square miles of territory and had placed our army in a favorable situation for future operations . . .
>
> This striking victory completely demonstrated the wisdom of building up a distinct American army. No form of propaganda could overcome the depressing effect on the enemy's morale of the fact that a new adversary had been able to put a formidable army in the field against him which, in its first offensive, could win such an important engagement. This result, after nearly a year and a half of working and waiting, must have tremendously heartened our people at home, as it gave them a tangible reason to believe that our contribution to the war would be the deciding factor. It inspired our troops with unlimited confidence which was to stand them in good stead against the weary days and nights of battle they were to experience later on. The St. Mihiel victory probably did more than any single operation of the war to encourage the tired Allies. After the years of doubt and despair, of suffering and loss, it brought them assurance of the final defeat of an enemy whose armies had seemed well-nigh invincible. The French people of all classes were loud in their praise of Americans.
>
> —John J. Pershing, commander of the American Expeditionary Force
> *My Experiences in the World War*

1. How did the victory at St. Mihiel benefit the U.S. military forces in France?

_____

_____

2. How did the Battle of St. Mihiel affect the mood of the Germans, the Allies, and Americans at home?

_____

_____

_____

DOCUMENT 7

Before You Read The following words in the document below may be
new to you: *reconnaissance, arduous*. You may want to use a dictionary to
look them up.

In relinquishing command of the air troops of the 1st Army, I desire to
express my admiration and appreciation for the manner in which their duty
has been performed by the whole command. You came into full battle a
new and untried organization. You served shoulder to shoulder with our
French, British and Italian Allies. You have shot down and destroyed two
hundred sixty-one airplanes and thirty balloons. You have covered the
army while it has been attacking, marching and holding its positions. Your
reconnaissance has extended over the enemy's whole position to a great
depth, both night and day, and you have worked smoothly and
energetically with our Allies, and have met the best air troops the enemy
possesses, and destroyed them . . .

In all your work remember the arduous duties of the troops on the
ground. When you are freezing in the air, they are wading over the
battlefields deep in mud and debris; when you are getting the enemy's
tracer bullets and anti-aircraft fire through your planes, they are going
through the artillery and machine gun fire below you. Their losses
correspond to yours. You must protect them and show them the way
forward. Work closely with them, because only by the combined work of
all arms will our full power be developed.

—Brigadier General William Mitchell
Chief of Air Service, First Army, American Expeditionary Force
Order given as he took up a new command, October 21, 1918

---

1. What were the two main messages that General William Mitchell wanted to convey
   to the air troops?

   _____

   _____

   _____

2. What were some of the accomplishments of the Air Service of the U.S. First Army?

   _____

   _____

   _____

Activity 8   Document-Based Activity

Writing a Document-Based Essay

HISTORICAL CONTEXT When World War I began in Europe in August 1914, the United States declared its neutrality. In practice, however, American trade policies favored the Allied nations. U.S. commerce with Britain and France tripled, while trade with Germany nearly disappeared. In January 1917 Germany started targeting all merchant ships destined for Britain. After German submarines sank several American vessels, the United States declared war on Germany in April 1917. A year and a half later the Allies finally defeated the Central Powers.

TASK Using information from the documents and your knowledge of American history, write an essay in which you:

- Explain how the United States contributed to the Allied war effort during World War I.

- Discuss the role America played in determining the outcome of the conflict.

Part B

DIRECTIONS Using the information from the documents provided and your knowledge of American history, write a well-organized essay that includes an introduction, a body of several paragraphs, and a conclusion. In the body of the essay, use examples from at least *four* documents. Support your response with relevant facts, examples, and details. Include additional outside information.

GUIDELINES
In your essay, be sure to:

- Address all aspects of the **Task** by accurately analyzing and interpreting at least *four* documents.

- Incorporate information from the documents in the body of the essay.

- Incorporate relevant outside information.

- Support the theme with relevant facts, examples, and details.

- Use a logical and clear plan of organization.

- Introduce the theme by establishing a framework that is beyond a simple statement of the **Task** or **Historical Context**.

- Conclude the essay with a summation of the theme.

Activity 9

Document-Based Activity

The Roaring Twenties

Using Source Materials

HISTORICAL CONTEXT Many Americans were troubled by the social and economic changes of the early 1900s. Waves of immigrants brought unfamiliar values and customs. Large bureaucratic corporations created a complex, impersonal work culture. In response to these changes, people drew inspiration from the dramatic successes of larger-than-life celebrity heroes. The mass media of the 1920s fueled this trend. Movies, radio, and newspapers glorified the stars of the entertainment and sports worlds.

TASK Using information from the documents and your knowledge of American history, answer the questions that follow each document in Part A. Your answers to the questions will help you write the Part B essay.

Part A

DIRECTIONS Examine the following documents and answer the short-answer questions that follow each document.

DOCUMENT 1

> There is no agency so fraught with possibilities for service of good or evil to the American people as the radio . . . The power of the press will not be comparable to that of broadcasting stations when the industry is fully developed. If the development continues as rapidly in the future as in the past, it will only be a few years before these broadcasting stations . . . will simultaneously reach an audience of over half our citizenship, and bring messages to the fireside of nearly every home in America.
>
> —Representative Luther A. Johnson
> Speech to the U.S. House of Representatives, March 13, 1926

1. According to Representative Luther A. Johnson, how does the power of radio compare to that of newspapers?

_____

_____

2. How does Johnson seem to feel about the developing radio industry?

_____

_____

Activity 9   Document-Based Activity

DOCUMENT 2

Before You Read The following words in the document below may be
new to you: *facilitated*, *tangential*, *flacks*, *quintessence*. You may want to
use a dictionary to look them up.

In a culture preoccupied with personality, "celebrity" became a measure of
success. But even more important to the rise of celebrity, and what in fact
facilitated this rise, was the centralization of the entertainment industry in
New York between 1900 and 1929. For all kinds of entertainment . . . New
York emerged as the central market in these decades. Star personality
celebrities fueled this energetic commercial culture, and in fact became that
culture's icons . . . promoted by tangential industries that grew up around
the entertainment industry. New "brokers," such as theatrical agents and
public relations flacks, by the late 1920s had constructed what one witness
called a "staggering machine of desire" that centered on celebrity . . .

One way to measure America's shift away from a hero-oriented stance
to an embrace of celebrity was . . . to survey the biographical articles that
appeared in *The Saturday Evening Post* and *Colliers* between 1901 and
1941: in the years from 1901–1914, 74 percent of the subjects came from
traditional fields such as politics, business, and the professions. But after
1922 over half came from the world of entertainment: sports figures like
Joe Louis and Babe Ruth, and movie stars such as Gloria Swanson and
Charlie Chaplin. The machinery providing mass information—the new
broker network and the flourishing print, broadcasting, recording, and film
industries—created a ravenous market for celebrity culture . . .

In the 1920s and '30s, Hollywood celebrities came to represent the
quintessence of glamour. Packaging star imagery became a major
component of the Hollywood dream machine: the enduring images of the
stars . . . were the portraits made by each studio for publicity purposes.

—Amy Henderson, historian at the Smithsonian Institution
"Media and the Rise of Celebrity Culture," *OAH Magazine of History*

---

1. According to the article, how did Americans' interests change in the early 1900s?

_____

_____

2. What factors contributed to the rise of a celebrity culture in the 1920s?

_____

_____

Document-Based Activity
The Roaring Twenties

DOCUMENT 3
Jack Dempsey–Georges Carpentier heavyweight boxing championship bout, Jersey City, New Jersey, July 2, 1921

© Bettmann/CORBIS

1. What can you infer from this photograph about sports in America in the 1920s?

_____

_____

_____

2. How did events like the one pictured above contribute to the rise of celebrities in America?

_____

_____

_____

Activity 9   Document-Based Activity

The Roaring Twenties

DOCUMENT 4

Before You Read The following words in the document below may be
new to you: *precipice, panorama.* You may want to use a dictionary to
look them up.

Outlined against a blue-gray October sky, the Four Horsemen rode again.
In dramatic lore they are known as Famine, Pestilence, Destruction and
Death. These are only aliases. Their real names are Stuhldreher, Miller,
Crowley and Layden. They formed the crest of the South Bend cyclone
before which another fighting Army football team was swept over the
precipice at the Polo Grounds yesterday afternoon as 55,000 spectators
peered down on the bewildering panorama spread on the green plain
below.

A cyclone can't be snared. It may be surrounded but somewhere it
breaks through to keep on going. When the cyclone starts from South
Bend, where the candle lights still gleam through the Indiana sycamores,
those in the way must take to storm cellars at top speed.

Yesterday the cyclone struck again as Notre Dame beat the Army, 13 to
7, with a set of backfield stars that ripped and crashed through a strong
Army defense with more speed and power than the warring cadets could
meet . . .

The Army has a better team than it had last year. So has Notre Dame.
We doubt that any team in the country could have beaten Rockne's array
yesterday afternoon, East or West. It was a great football team brilliantly
directed, a team of speed, power and team play. The Army has no cause to
gloom over its showing. It played first-class football against more speed
than it could match.

Those who have tackled a cyclone can understand.

—Grantland Rice
New York Herald-Tribune, October 19, 1924

---

1. How did Grantland Rice describe the Notre Dame football players? What effect do
   you think his article had on those who read it?

   _____

   _____

2. Why do you think Rice wrote the article the way that he did?

   _____

   _____

Activity 9

Document-Based Activity
The Roaring Twenties

DOCUMENT 5
Premiere of *The Jazz Singer* at Warners' Theatre, New York City, 1927

The Granger Collection, New York

1. Look closely at the photograph. What devices do you see that are intended to entice people to see the movie?

   _____

   _____

2. The Jazz Singer was the first sound movie ever made. What does the size of the crowd in front of the theatre suggest about interest in this film?

   _____

   _____

Activity 9

Document-Based Activity
The Roaring Twenties

DOCUMENT 6

Less than four weeks ago, "Slim" Lindbergh, a curiously simple, silent young air mail pilot, left this vicinity at gloomy dawn, alone in his plane, Spirit of St. Louis, bound for Paris, across the ocean. Not more than 2,000 men and women saw him go.

Yesterday, he returned to a tribute of millions. Le Bourget and Croyden, with their hysterical, unwieldy crowds; Paris, with its Boulevard throngs, and Washington with its glitter of formality were all but obliterated by the greetings of New York.

Certainly, this city never has seen the counterpart of yesterday. Police estimate 4,300,000 persons were in the streets, on the roofs or draped from windows, from the Battery to the grandstand in Central Park. It seems an exaggerated figure, but none who passed through the double wall of humans along the route of the parade would quarrel over a difference of a million or so.

Nor was the parade, which passed mile after mile through air thick with confetti and torn paper, the most striking spectacle of the day. That remained when the day was over, the journey up the bay from the Narrows, with the ruffle-haired Lindbergh on the bridge of the reception boat, Macom, and behind, churning the dull green water, an armada such as it is given to few men to see . . .

Lindbergh—"Slim" Lindbergh—was at the head of the procession, standing, nervous and, for the only time during the day, obviously excited on the bridge of the slim Macom, the sun touching his blond hair, his strong fingers twisted about the guardrail. A faint smile parted his lips. It went, then came, then went again, as if he were doing his very best to look as if he was used to extraordinary goings on.

—Oliver H. P. Garrett,
New York World, May 22, 1927

1. Who was the subject of this celebration? Why were the people celebrating?

_____

_____

2. What can you conclude from this article about how Americans felt about their heroes in the 1920s?

_____

_____

DOCUMENT 7

Before You Read The following words in the document below may be new to you: *hitherto, southpaw, momentous, audible, permeated.* You may want to use a dictionary to look them up.

Babe Ruth scaled the hitherto unattained heights yesterday. Home run 60, a terrific smash off the southpaw pitching of Zachary, nestled in the Babe's favorite spot in the right field bleachers, and before the roar had ceased it was found that this drive not only had made home run record history, but also was the winning margin in a 4 to 2 victory over the Senators. This also was the Yanks' 109th triumph of the season. Their last league game of the year will be played today.

When the Babe stepped to the plate in that momentous eighth inning the score was deadlocked. Koenig was on third base, the result of a triple, one man was out and all was tense . . .

The Babe took a vicious swing at the third pitched ball and the bat connected with a crash that was audible in all parts of the stand. It was not necessary to follow the course of the ball. The boys in the bleachers indicated the route of the record homer. It dropped about half way to the top. Boys, No. 60 was some homer, a fitting wallop to top the Babe's record of 59 in 1921.

While the crowd cheered and the Yankee players roared their greetings the Babe made his triumphant, almost regal tour of the paths. He jogged around slowly, touched each bag firmly and carefully, and when he embedded his spikes in the rubber disk to record officially homer 60, hats were tossed liberally and the spirit of celebration permeated the place.

The Babe's stroll out to his position was the signal for a handkerchief salute in which all the bleacherites, to the last man, participated. Jovial Babe entered into the carnival spirit and punctuated his Ringly strides with a succession of snappy military salutes.

—*New York Times*, October 1, 1927

1. What was Babe Ruth's profession? How is he described in the article?

_____

_____

2. What was special about Ruth's accomplishment?

_____

_____

Activity 9

Document-Based Activity

The Roaring Twenties

Writing a Document-Based Essay

HISTORICAL CONTEXT Many Americans were troubled by the social and economic changes of the early 1900s. Waves of immigrants brought unfamiliar values and customs. Large bureaucratic corporations created a complex, impersonal work culture. In response to these changes, people drew inspiration from the dramatic successes of larger-than-life celebrity heroes. The mass media of the 1920s fueled this trend. Movies, radio, and newspapers, glorified the stars of the entertainment and sports worlds.

TASK Using information from the documents and your knowledge of American history, write an essay in which you:

- Explain why celebrities and heroes became increasingly important to Americans in the 1920s.

- Discuss how celebrities and heroes inspired Americans during that decade.

Part B

DIRECTIONS Using the information from the documents provided and your knowledge of American history, write a well-organized essay that includes an introduction, a body of several paragraphs, and a conclusion. In the body of the essay, use examples from at least *four* documents. Support your response with relevant facts, examples, and details. Include additional outside information.

GUIDELINES
In your essay, be sure to:

- Address all aspects of the **Task** by accurately analyzing and interpreting at least *four* documents.

- Incorporate information from the documents in the body of the essay.

- Incorporate relevant outside information.

- Support the theme with relevant facts, examples, and details.

- Use a logical and clear plan of organization.

- Introduce the theme by establishing a framework that is beyond a simple statement of the **Task** or **Historical Context**.

- Conclude the essay with a summation of the theme.

Activity 10

Document-Based Activity

The Great Depression

Using Source Materials

HISTORICAL CONTEXT In October 1929 the United States entered the worst economic depression in the nation's history. Stock prices plummeted as investors lost confidence in the American economy. Banks and businesses failed. One fourth of the labor force was out of work. To make matters worse, drought and dust storms wiped out thousands of farms in the Midwest in the 1930s. People across the nation struggled to escape the grip of poverty. Millions of Americans desperately searched for ways to provide for themselves and their families.

TASK Using information from the documents and your knowledge of American history, answer the questions that follow each document in Part A. Your answers to the questions will help you write the Part B essay.

Part A

DIRECTIONS Examine the following documents and answer the short-answer questions that follow each document.

DOCUMENT 1

> I told my dad I wasn't going to school any more. He said: Why, you just come on and go work with me. I went in the mines, and I went to work. From '31 to about the last of '32 . . . We lived eight miles from the mine, and we had to ride it horseback . . . Many times I'd have to git off and hammer his feet out of the stirrups. They'd be froze in the stirrups . . . We got up at five in the mornin', start at six. We got out at ten that night. We'd work about sixteen hours a day, seventeen hours.
>
> —Buddy Blankenship, West Virginia miner
> *Hard Times: An Oral History of the Great Depression*

1. Why do you think Buddy Blankenship's father allowed him to quit school and take a job in the mines?

_____

2. How do you think Blankenship's mining experiences compared to his experiences as a student?

_____

_____

Document-Based Activities

Activity 10

Document-Based Activity

The Great Depression

DOCUMENT 2

Before You Read The following word in the document below may be new to you: *foundry*. You may want to use a dictionary to look it up.

1929 was pretty hard. I hoboed, I bummed, I begged for a nickel to get somethin' to eat. Go get a job, oh, at the foundry there. They didn't hire me because I didn't belong to the right kind of race. 'Nother time I went into Saginaw, it was two white fellas and myself made three. The fella there hired the two men and didn't hire me. I was back out on the streets . . .

When I was hoboing, I would lay on the side of the tracks and wait until I could see the train comin'. I would always carry a bottle of water in my pocket and a piece of tape or rag to keep it from bustin' and put a piece of bread in my pocket, so I wouldn't starve on the way. I would ride all day and all night long in the hot sun . . .

I was in chain gangs and been in jail all over the country. I was in a chain gang in Georgia. I had to pick cotton for four months, for just hoboin' on a train . . . They gave me thirty-five cents and a pair of overalls when I got out . . .

I knocked on people's doors. They'd say, "What do you want? I'll call the police." And they'd put you in jail for vag[rancy]. They'd make you milk cows, thirty or ninety days. Up in Wisconsin, they'd do the same thing. Alabama, they'd do the same thing. California, anywhere you'd go. Always in jail, and I never did nothin'.

A man had to be on the road. Had to leave his wife, had to leave his mother, leave his family just to try to get money to live on. But he think: my dear mother, tryin' to send her money, worryin' how she's starvin'.

The shame I was feeling. I walked out because I didn't have a job. I said, "I'm goin' out in the world and get me a job." And God help me, I couldn't get anything.

—Louis Banks
Hard Times: An Oral History of the Great Depression

---

1. Why did Louis Banks leave home during the Great Depression?

_____

_____

2. How did other people treat Banks? Why do you think he was treated this way?

_____

_____

Document-Based Activities

Activity 10

Document-Based Activity

The Great Depression

DOCUMENT 3
Washington, D.C., December 19, 1930

© Bettmann/CORBIS

1. What is happening in this picture? Why do you think these people are engaging in this activity?

_____

_____

_____

2. What is significant about the location shown in the picture?

_____

_____

_____

Document-Based Activities

Activity 10

Document-Based Activity

The Great Depression

DOCUMENT 4

We lost everything. It was the time I would collect four, five hundred dollars a week. After that, I couldn't collect fifteen, ten dollars a week. I was going around trying to collect enough money to keep my family going. Very few people could pay you. Maybe a dollar if they would feel sorry for you or what.

We tried to struggle along living day by day. Then I couldn't pay the rent. I had a little car, but I couldn't pay no license for it. I left it parked against the court. I sold it for $15 in order to buy some food for the family. I had three little children. It was a time when I didn't even have money to buy a pack of cigarettes, and I was a smoker. I didn't have a nickel in my pocket.

Finally people started to talk me into going into the relief. They had open soup kitchens. Al Capone, he had open soup kitchens somewhere downtown, where people were standing in line. And you had to go two blocks, stand there, around the corner, to get a bowl of soup . . .

I didn't want to go on relief. Believe me, when I was forced to go to the office of the relief, the tears were running out of my eyes. I couldn't bear myself to take money from anybody for nothing. If it wasn't for those kids . . . many a time it came to my mind to go commit suicide . . .

I went to the relief and they, after a lotta red tape and investigation, they gave me $45 a month. Out of that $45 we had to pay rent, we had to buy food and clothing for the children. So how long can that $45 go? I was paying $30 on the rent. I went and find another a cheaper flat, stove heat, for $15 a month. I'm telling you, today a dog wouldn't live in that type of a place. Such a dirty, filthy, dark place.

—Ben Isaacs, clothing salesman
Hard Times: An Oral History of the Great Depression

1. How did Ben Isaacs' economic situation change when the Great Depression occurred?

   _____

   _____

2. What did Isaacs do to provide for his family during the Depression?

   _____

   _____

Activity 10

Document-Based Activity

The Great Depression

DOCUMENT 5
Hooverville in Washington, D.C., 1932

1. What is the purpose of the display shown in the picture?

   _____

   _____

   _____

2. What can you conclude about the parents of these children? How do you think they felt about President Herbert Hoover?

   _____

   _____

   _____

Document-Based Activity

The Great Depression

DOCUMENT 6

Before You Read The following words in the document below may be
new to you: *invariable, munificent, multifarious, precariously.* You may
want to use a dictionary to look them up.

The Bronx Slave Market! What is it? Who are its dealers? Who are its
victims? What are its causes? How far does its stench spread? . . .

Rain or shine, cold or hot, you will find them there—Negro women, old
and young . . . with the invariable paper bundle, waiting expectantly for
Bronx housewives to buy their strength and energy for an hour, two hours,
or even for a day at the munificent rate of fifteen, twenty, twenty-five, or,
if luck be with them, thirty cents an hour . . .

In the boom days before the onslaught of the depression in 1929, many
of these women who are now forced to bargain for day's work on street
corners, were employed in grand homes in the rich Eighties, or in wealthier
homes in Long Island and Westchester, at more than adequate wages.
Some are former marginal industrial workers, forced by the slack in
industry to seek other means of sustenance . . . But whatever their
standing prior to the depression, none sought employment where they now
seek it . . . They come to the Bronx . . . largely in desperation . . .

She who is fortunate (?) . . . is led away to perform hours of multifarious
household drudgeries. Under a rigid watch, she is permitted to scrub floors
on her bended knees, to hang precariously from window sills, cleaning
window after window, or to strain and sweat over steaming tubs of heavy
blankets, spreads and furniture covers.

Fortunate, indeed, is she who gets the full hourly rate promised. Often,
her day's slavery is rewarded with a single dollar bill or whatever her
unscrupulous employer pleases to pay. More often, the clock is set back for
an hour or more. Too often she is sent away without any pay at all.

—Ella Baker and Marvel Cooke
The Crisis (November 1935)

---

1. According to the authors of the article, what was the Bronx Slave Market?

_____

_____

2. What does the article suggest about race relations during the Great Depression?

_____

_____

Activity 10

Document-Based Activity

The Great Depression

DOCUMENT 7

Before You Read The following word in the document below may be new
to you: *jalopies*. You may want to use a dictionary to look it up.

> The drought continued acute during much of 1936. Oklahoma farms
> became great dunes of shifting sand . . .
>
> Westward fled the refugees from this new Sahara, as if obedient to the
> old American tradition that westward lies the land of promise. In 1934 and
> 1935 Californians became aware of an increasing influx into their state of
> families and groups of families of "Okies," traveling in ancient family
> jalopies; but for years the streams of humanity continued to run . . .
>
> And when these varied streams of migrants reached the Coast they
> found themselves in desperate competition for jobs with individuals or
> families who for years had been "fruit tramps," moving northward each
> year with the harvests from the Imperial Valley in southern California to
> the Sacramento Valley or even to the apple-picking in the Yakima Valley
> in Washington.
>
> Here in the land of promise, agriculture had long been partly
> industrialized. Huge farms were in the control of absentee owners or banks
> or corporations, and were accustomed to depend upon the labor of
> migratory "fruit tramps," who had formerly been mostly Mexicans,
> Japanese, and other foreigners, but now were increasingly Americans.
> Those laborers who were lucky enough to get jobs picking cotton or peas
> or fruit would be sheltered temporarily in camps . . . These pickers were
> homeless, voteless nomads, unwanted anywhere save at the harvest season.
>
> When wave after wave of the new migrants reached California, the labor
> market became glutted, earnings were low, and jobs became so scarce that
> groups of poverty-stricken families would be found squatting in makeshift
> Hoovervilles or bunking miserably in their . . . old Fords by the roadside.
>
> —Frederick Lewis Allen
> *Since Yesterday*

1. Why did large numbers of people move west to California in the 1930s?

_____

_____

2. What was life like for the Midwesterners who reached California?

_____

_____

Document-Based Activity

The Great Depression

Writing a Document-Based Essay

HISTORICAL CONTEXT In October 1929 the United States entered the worst economic depression in the nation's history. Stock prices plummeted as investors lost confidence in the American economy. Banks and businesses failed. One fourth of the labor force was out of work. To make matters worse, drought and dust storms wiped out thousands of farms in the Midwest in the 1930s. People across the nation struggled to escape the grip of poverty. Millions of Americans desperately searched for ways to provide for themselves and their families.

TASK Using information from the documents and your knowledge of American history, write an essay in which you:

- Explain how the Great Depression affected Americans.

- Describe the different ways that people tried to cope with the economic disaster.

Part B

DIRECTIONS Using the information from the documents provided and your knowledge of American history, write a well-organized essay that includes an introduction, a body of several paragraphs, and a conclusion. In the body of the essay, use examples from at least *four* documents. Support your response with relevant facts, examples, and details. Include additional outside information.

GUIDELINES
In your essay, be sure to:

- Address all aspects of the **Task** by accurately analyzing and interpreting at least *four* documents.

- Incorporate information from the documents in the body of the essay.

- Incorporate relevant outside information.

- Support the theme with relevant facts, examples, and details.

- Use a logical and clear plan of organization.

- Introduce the theme by establishing a framework that is beyond a simple statement of the **Task** or **Historical Context**.

- Conclude the essay with a summation of the theme.

Document-Based Activities

Activity 11

Document-Based Activity

The New Deal

Using Source Materials

HISTORICAL CONTEXT Soon after becoming president in March 1933, Franklin Roosevelt convinced Congress to pass his New Deal reform program to fight the Great Depression. The government appropriated over $500 million in relief funds for the starving. Congress then set up agencies such as the Civilian Conservation Corps (CCC) and Works Progress Administration (WPA) to provide work for the jobless. The New Deal also created planning agencies to revive the economy. Despite these ambitious efforts, the New Deal drew strong opposition. Some critics said Roosevelt did too little, while others said he did too much.

TASK Using information from the documents and your knowledge of American history, answer the questions that follow each document in Part A. Your answers to the questions will help you write the Part B essay.

Part A

DIRECTIONS Examine the following documents and answer the short-answer questions that follow each document.

DOCUMENT 1

> We are suppose to get $55.00. a month . . . $55.00 a month is too small amount for a man and his family to live on without any other help, when he have to pay just as small as $12.50 at the lowest rent, and buy coal, food, clothes, medicine or doctor bill and other expenses . . . if we continue to get paid like this, it will be that lots of us to be set out on the streets, and will have a hard way to get anywhere to stay.
>
> —Public Works Administration (PWA) worker in Chicago
> Letter to President Franklin Roosevelt, December 11, 1935

1. What problem did this PWA worker face?

_____

_____

2. What do you think this PWA worker wanted to accomplish by writing this letter?

_____

_____

Activity 11   Document-Based Activity

The New Deal

DOCUMENT 2

Before You Read The following words in the document below may be new to you: *heeding, restive, partisan*. You may want to use a dictionary to look them up.

My daily job is to shuttle between government and business, trying to explain government to business, working primarily in the interest of business.

I spend my mornings talking to businessmen callers . . . listening to their troubles, suggesting courses which are in line, or not too far out of line, with government policies . . .

If all the views of all the businessmen could be condensed into a brief address to Washington, perhaps the address would be something like this:

We know you have a hard job. We recognize the necessity for reforms, some of which must affect us. But you are forcing reforms on us faster than we can digest them . . . We accept your general leadership in the emergency, but we find your orders vague, and we don't know just what to do. Can't you reduce your program to something a little more definite, and tell us what it is, so that we may know how to plan ahead? If you will do this, we in turn will immediately increase our business, and provide more jobs than you are providing, and end the depression more quickly than you are ending it.

But the government shows few signs of heeding the pleas of business . . . business sentiment is becoming more restive, more impatient, more disposed to abandon its previous timidity. The movement will come to a head some time late this year. It will have nothing to do with the elections. It will not be partisan. It will be evident in a burst of "plain speaking" from various business groups. Some people will call it a "business revolt."

—W.M. Kiplinger
"Why Business Men Fear Washington"
Scribner's (October 1934)

1. According to W.M. Kiplinger, how did business leaders feel about the New Deal?

_____

_____

2. What two possible outcomes did Kiplinger seem to be predicting for the future?

_____

_____

Activity 11   Document-Based Activity

                                        The New Deal

DOCUMENT 3

Before You Read The following word in the document below may be new
to you: *plutocrats*. You may want to use a dictionary to look it up.

It is not out of place for me to say that the support which I brought to Mr.
Roosevelt to secure his nomination and election as President . . . was on the
assurances which I had that he would take the proper stand for the
redistribution of wealth in the campaign. He did that much in the
campaign; but after his election, what then? . . .

It was after my disappointment over the Roosevelt policy, after he
became President, that I saw the light. I soon began to understand that,
regardless of what we had been promised, our only chance of securing the
fulfillment of such pledges was to organize the men and the women of the
United States so that they were a force capable of action, and capable of
requiring such a policy from the lawmakers and from the President after
they took office. That was the beginning of the Share Our Wealth Society
movement . . .

Even after the present President of the United States had thrown down
the pledge which he had made time after time, and rather indicated the
desire, instead, to have all the common people of America fed from a half-
starvation dole, while the plutocrats of the United States were allowed to
wax richer and richer, even after that, I made the public proposition that if
he would return to his promise and carry out the pledge given to the people
and to me that, regardless of all that had passed, I would again support his
administration to the limit of my ability.

Of course, however, I was not blind; I had long since come to the
understanding that he was chained to . . . other interests which made
impossible his keeping the words which he uttered to the people.

—Huey P. Long, U.S. Senator
Circular to members of the Share Our Wealth Society

---

1. Why did Senator Huey Long at first support and then later oppose President Franklin
   Roosevelt?

   _____

   _____

2. According to Long, what was the purpose of the Share Our Wealth Society?

   _____

   _____

DOCUMENT 4

Before You Read The following words in the document below may be new to you: *castigated*, *usurers*, *plaudits*, *spurious*. You may want to use a dictionary to look them up.

At last, when the most brilliant minds amongst the industrialists, bankers and their kept politicians had failed to solve the cause of the needless depression, there appeared upon the scene of our national life a new champion of the people, Franklin Delano Roosevelt! . . .

With the whip of his scorn he castigated these usurers who exploited the poor . . . No man in modern times received such plaudits from the poor as did Franklin Roosevelt when he promised to drive the money-changers from the temple—the money-changers who had clipped the coins of wages, who had manufactured spurious money, and who had brought proud America to her knees.

March 4, 1933! I shall never forget the inaugural address, which seemed to re-echo the very words employed by Christ Himself as He actually drove the money-changers from the temple . . . But I am constrained to admit that "Roosevelt and ruin" is the order of the day, because the money-changers have not been driven from the temple . . .

. . . the Democratic platform is discredited before it is published. Was there not a 1932 platform? By Mr. Roosevelt and its colleagues, was it not regarded as a solemn pledge to the people? Certainly! [But] it was plowed under like the cotton, slaughtered like the pigs . . .

Alas! The temple still remains the private property of the money-changers. The golden key has been handed over to them for safekeeping— the key which now is fashioned in the shape of a double cross!

—Father Charles E. Coughlin
Radio address, "Roosevelt and Ruin," June 19, 1936

---

1. How did Father Charles Coughlin's assessment of President Franklin Roosevelt change over time?

   _____

   _____

2. How is Coughlin's address similar to and different from the passage in Document 3?

   _____

   _____

Document-Based Activities

Document-Based Activity

The New Deal

DOCUMENT 5

I suppose from your point of view the work relief, old age pensions, slum clearance and all the rest seems like a perfect remedy for all the ills of this country, but I would like you to see the results, as the other half see them.

We have always had a shiftless, never-do-well class of people whose one and only aim in life is to live without work. I have . . . tried to help some of the most promising and have seen others try to help them, but it can't be done. We cannot help those who will not try to help themselves and if they do try a square deal is all they need, and by the way that is all this country needs or ever has needed: a square deal for all and then, let each one paddle their own canoe, or sink.

There has never been any necessity for any one who is able to work, being on relief in this locality, but there have been many eating the bread of charity and they have lived better than ever before. I have had taxpayers tell me that their children came from school and asked why they couldn't have nice lunches like the children on relief . . .

During the worst of the depression many of the farmers had to deny their families butter, eggs, meat etc. and sell it to pay their taxes and then had to stand by and see the dead-beats carry it home to their families by the arm load, and they knew their tax money was helping pay for it . . . The crookedness, selfishness, greed and graft of the crooked politicians is making one gigantic racket out of the new deal and it is making this a nation of dead-beats and beggars and if it continues the people who will work will soon be nothing but slaves for the pampered poverty rats and I am afraid these human parasites are going to become a menace to the country unless they are disfranchised . . .

Is it any wonder the taxpayers are discouraged by all this penalizing of thrift and industry to reward shiftlessness . . . ?

—M.A.H., a woman in Columbus, Indiana
Letter to Eleanor Roosevelt, December 14, 1937

1. What does the writer of the letter think of President Roosevelt's New Deal programs?

_____

_____

2. What does the letter writer suggest should be done with the relief programs?

_____

_____

DOCUMENT 6
"What Next?" *Jersey City Journal*, January 23, 1936

1. Who do you think the cartoonist portrayed President Roosevelt as a magician?

_____

_____

2. What point do you think the cartoonist was trying make?

_____

_____

Document-Based Activity

The New Deal

DOCUMENT 7

Before You Read The following word in the document below may be new
to you: *expedite*. You may want to use a dictionary to look it up.

President Roosevelt has cleverly camouflaged a most amazing and startling
proposal for packing the Supreme Court. It is true that the lower courts are
slow and overburdened, we probably do need more judges to expedite
litigation but this condition should not be used as a subtle excuse for
changing the complexion and undermining the independence of our highest
court. Increasing the number of judges from nine to fifteen would not make
this high tribunal act any more promptly than it does now, but it would
give the President control of the Judiciary Department . . .

The Supreme Court having declared invalid many of the administration
measures the President now resorts to a plan of creating a Supreme Court
that will be entirely sympathetic with his ideas. Provision has been made
for amending the Constitution. If [it] is necessary to change the
Constitution it should be done in the regular way. The President is
mistaken, if he thinks he can conceal his real purpose of packing,
influencing and controlling the Supreme Court by confusing that objective
with a long dissertation on the slow action of our various courts . . .

Our Government is composed of three departments, Legislative,
Executive and Judiciary . . . As a result of the election and the transfer of
powers by so-called emergency measures, the Executive now dominates
the Legislative Department. The President now proposes also to dominate
the Judiciary . . .

This proposal should give every American grave concern for it is a step
towards absolutism and complete dictatorial power.

—Frank E. Gannett, publisher of Gannett Newspapers
Statement, 1937

1. According to the article, what did President Franklin Roosevelt want to do? How did
he justify his proposal?

_____

_____

2. What did Frank E. Gannett think of Roosevelt's proposal? Why was his opinion
important?

_____

_____

Writing a Document-Based Essay

HISTORICAL CONTEXT Soon after becoming president in March 1933, Franklin Roosevelt convinced Congress to pass his New Deal reform program to fight the Great Depression. The government appropriated over $500 million in relief funds for the starving. Congress then set up agencies such as the Civilian Conservation Corps (CCC) and Works Progress Administration (WPA) to provide work for the jobless. The New Deal also created planning agencies to revive the economy. Despite these ambitious efforts, the New Deal drew strong opposition. Some critics said Roosevelt did too little, while others said he did too much.

TASK Using information from the documents and your knowledge of American history, write an essay in which you:

- Describe the criticisms leveled against the New Deal.

- Discuss the various reasons people had for opposing Franklin Roosevelt's agenda in the 1930s.

Part B

DIRECTIONS Using the information from the documents provided and your knowledge of American history, write a well-organized essay that includes an introduction, a body of several paragraphs, and a conclusion. In the body of the essay, use examples from at least *four* documents. Support your response with relevant facts, examples, and details. Include additional outside information.

GUIDELINES
In your essay, be sure to:

- Address all aspects of the **Task** by accurately analyzing and interpreting at least *four* documents.

- Incorporate information from the documents in the body of the essay.

- Incorporate relevant outside information.

- Support the theme with relevant facts, examples, and details.

- Use a logical and clear plan of organization.

- Introduce the theme by establishing a framework that is beyond a simple statement of the **Task** or **Historical Context**.

- Conclude the essay with a summation of the theme.

Activity 12

Document-Based Activity

The U.S. Response to the Holocaust

Using Source Materials

HISTORICAL CONTEXT Germany's persecution of Jews began in the 1930s but grew worse after the start of World War II. In 1941 Adolph Hitler secretly ordered a campaign of mass murder to eliminate all Jews in Europe. U.S. officials received news of this plan in the summer of 1942 but were slow to react. Then, in January 1944, President Franklin Roosevelt created a War Refugee Board to help Jews escape from Nazi-controlled Europe. The board helped save over 200,000 Jews, but the Nazi genocide claimed over 6 million lives in total. Critics charge that the United States could have done much more to help the victims of the Holocaust.

TASK Using information from the documents and your knowledge of American history, answer the questions that follow each document in Part A. Your answers to the questions will help you write the Part B essay.

Part A

DIRECTIONS Examine the following documents and answer the short-answer questions that follow each document.

DOCUMENT 1

> We can delay and effectively stop for a temporary period of indefinite length the number of immigrants into the United States. We could do this by simply advising our consuls to put every obstacle in the way and to require additional evidence and to resort to various administrative devices which would postpone and postpone and postpone the granting of the visas.
>
> —Breckinridge Long, Assistant Secretary of State
> Memo to State Department Officials, June 26, 1940

1. What was Long's attitude about allowing immigrants into the United States?

_____

_____

2. How do you think Long's position affected Jews living in Nazi-controlled Europe?

_____

_____

Activity 12

Document-Based Activity
The U.S. Response to the Holocaust

DOCUMENT 2

Before You Read The following words in the document below may be new to you: *nativist, subordinates, indifferent, agitators, quota*. You may want to use a dictionary to look them up.

During the horrifying years of the Holocaust, while the Nazis were killing thousands of Jews a day, the U.S. State Department official in charge of matters concerning European refugees was Breckinridge Long, an extreme nativist with a particular suspicion of Eastern Europeans. To make matters worse, Long's views were shared by many of his subordinates, most of whom showed themselves to be indifferent to the tragedy unfolding in Europe . . . Long himself was extremely paranoid and came to believe not only that he was constantly under attack from "the communists, extreme radicals, Jewish professional agitators, [and] refugee enthusiasts," but that his colleagues were conspiring against him as well. It's not surprising that with men like Long in control, very little would be done to help the Jews in Europe . . .

Ultimately, the effect of the immigration policies set by Long's department was that, during American involvement in the war, 90 percent of the quota places available to immigrants from countries under German and Italian control were never filled. If they had been, an additional 190,000 people could have escaped the atrocities being committed by the Nazis.

Biographical Entry on Breckinridge Long
From the documentary, *America and the Holocaust*

1. According to the biographical entry, why did Assistant Secretary of State Breckinridge Long not do more to help the Jews in Europe during World War II?

_____

_____

_____

2. If all of the quota places available to immigrants from countries under German and Italian control during the war had been filled, how many additional Europeans could have come to the United States and have been saved from Nazi atrocities?

_____

_____

Activity 12

Document-Based Activity

The U.S. Response to the Holocaust

DOCUMENT 3

Before You Read The following words in the document below may be
new to you: *agitation*, *exterminate*, *allegedly*. You may want to use a
dictionary to look them up.

> This morning Mr. Gerhart M. RIEGNER, secretary of the World Jewish
> Congress in Geneva, called in great agitation. He stated that he had just
> received a report from a German businessman of considerable prominence,
> who is said to have excellent political and military connections in Germany
> and from whom reliable and important political information has been
> obtained on two previous occasions, to the effect that there has been and is
> being considered in Hitler's headquarters a plan to exterminate all Jews
> from Germany and German-controlled areas in Europe after they have
> been concentrated in the east (presumably Poland). The number involved is
> said to be between three-and-a-half and four millions and the object is to
> permanently settle the Jewish question in Europe. The mass execution if
> decided upon would allegedly take place this fall.
>
> —Howard Elting, Jr.
> American Vice Consul, American Consulate, Geneva, Switzerland
> Letter to the U.S. Secretary of State, August 10, 1942

September 1935 Nazis enact the Nuremberg Laws, which, among other things, deprive German Jews of the right to vote, hold public office, and marry non-Jews.

January 1939 Adolf Hitler declares, "If the international Jewish financiers . . . should again succeed in plunging the nations into a world war the result will be . . . the annihilation of the Jewish race throughout Europe."

June 1942 The World Jewish Congress announces its estimate that the Nazis have already killed over a million Jews.

| 1935 | | 1937 | | 1939 | | 1941 | |

November 1938 Kristallnacht riots break out in Germany; nearly 100 Jews are killed and thousands of Jewish businesses are vandalized.

November 1940 The Warsaw ghetto is created, where 500,000 Jews are forced to live in a 1.5-square-mile area.

September 1941 German Special Action Groups massacre over 33,000 people, mostly Jews, outside Kiev, Ukraine.

1. According to the U.S. vice consul, what did Gerhart Riegner believe was going to
   happen in German-controlled Europe?

   _____

   _____

2. Do you think that State Department officials in August 1942 had good reasons to
   believe Riegner? Why or why not?

   _____

   _____

   _____

Activity 12

Document-Based Activity

The U.S. Response to the Holocaust

DOCUMENT 4

Before You Read The following words in the document below may be
new to you: *unprecedented, unabated, subjugate, notorious.* You may want
to use a dictionary to look them up.

It is a fact beyond denial that the Germans have deliberately and
systematically murdered millions of innocent civilians—Jews and
Christians alike—all over Europe. This campaign of terror and brutality,
which is unprecedented in all history and which even now continues
unabated, is part of a German plan to subjugate the free peoples of the
world. . . .

The War Refugee Board is engaged in a desperate effort to save as many
as possible of Hitler's intended victims. . . .

Recently the Board received from a representative close to the scene two
eyewitness accounts of events which occurred in notorious extermination
camps established by the Germans. The first report is based upon the
experiences of two young Slovakian Jews who escaped in April, 1944 after
spending two years in the Nazi concentration camps at Auschwitz and
Birkenau in southwestern Poland. The Second Report is made by a non-
Jewish Polish major, the only survivor of one group imprisoned at
Auschwitz. . . .

The Board has every reason to believe that these reports present a true
picture of the frightful happenings in these camps.

—War Refugee Board
November 1944

---

1. What was the desperate effort in which the War Refugee Board was engaged?

_____

_____

2. How did the War Refugee Board learn about the German extermination camps?

_____

_____

_____

Activity 12   # Document-Based Activity

The U.S. Response to the Holocaust

DOCUMENT 5

Before You Read The following words in the document below may be
new to you: *precision, allegedly.* You may want to use a dictionary to look
them up.

I refer to your letter of November 8th, in which you forwarded the report of
two eye-witnesses on the notorious German concentration and
extermination camps of Auschwitz and Birkenau in Upper Silesia.

The Operation Staff of the War Department has given careful consideration
to your suggestion that the bombing of these camps be undertaken. In
consideration of this proposal the following points were brought out:

a. Positive destruction of these camps would necessitate precision
bombing, employing heavy or medium bombardment, or attack by low
flying or dive bombing aircraft, preferably the latter.

b. The target is beyond the maximum range of medium bombardment, dive
bombers and fighter bombers located in United Kingdom, France or Italy.

c. Use of heavy bombardment from United Kingdom bases would
necessitate a hazardous round trip unescorted of approximately 2,000 miles
over enemy territory.

d. At the present critical stage of the war in Europe, our strategic air forces
are engaged in the destruction of industrial target systems vital to the
dwindling war potential of the enemy, from which they should not be
diverted. The positive solution to this problem is the earliest possible
victory over Germany, to which end we should exert our entire means.

                              —John McCloy, Assistant Secretary of War
                    Letter to John W. Pehle, Director, War Refugee Board
                                                  November 18, 1944

1. What did John Pehle, the director of the War Refugee Board, want the War
   Department to do?

   _____

   _____

2. What reasons did Asst. Secretary of War McCloy give for rejecting Pehle's request?

   _____

   _____

Activity 12   Document-Based Activity

The U.S. Response to the Holocaust

DOCUMENT 6

After a study it became apparent that such an operation [the bombing of the Auschwitz gas chambers and crematoria] could be executed only by the diversion of considerable air support essential to the success of our forces now engaged in decisive operations elsewhere and would in any case be of such doubtful efficacy that it would not warrant the use of our resources.

—John McCloy, Assistant Secretary of War
Letter to A. Leon Kubowitzki, World Jewish Congress
August 14, 1944

On Sunday, August 20 [1944] . . . 127 Flying Fortresses, escorted by 100 Mustang fighters, dropped 1,336 500-pound high-explosive bombs on the factory areas of Auschwitz, *less than five miles* to the east of the gas chambers . . .

Again, on September 13, a force of heavy bombers rained destruction on the factory areas of Auschwitz. The 96 Liberators encountered no German aircraft, but ground fire was heavy and brought three of them down. As before, no attempt was made to strike the killing installations . . .

On August 27, another 350 heavy bombers struck Blechhamer. Two days after that, 218 hit Moravska Ostrava and Oderberg (Bohum), both within forty-five miles of Auschwitz . . . On August 7, heavy bombers had carried out attacks on both sides of Auschwitz on the same day: 357 had bombed Blechhammer, and 55 had hit Trzebinia, only thirteen miles northeast of Auschwitz.

—David S. Wyman
The Abandonment of the Jews

1. How do the passages from *The Abandonment of the Jews* challenge Asst. Secretary of War McCloy's response to A. Leon Kubowitzki?

_____

_____

2. What claim in McCloy's letter is not challenged by these particular passages from *The Abandonment of the Jews?* What fact in the second paragraph of these passages might someone use to argue against bombing the gas chambers at Auschwitz?

_____

_____

Activity 12

Document-Based Activity

The U.S. Response to the Holocaust

DOCUMENT 7

USHMM, courtesy of Arnold Bauer Barach

1. In April and May 1945, American forces liberated several German concentration camps. In this photo, surviving inmates of one of these camps show their American liberators the crematoria that were used to burn the bodies of inmates who had been gassed. If American policymakers had seen images like this earlier in the war, do you think they would have pursued different policies? Explain.

_____

_____

_____

2. If the American public had seen images like this one earlier in the war, do you think there would have been greater pressure on the U.S. government to help more Jewish refugees in Europe reach America? Explain.

_____

_____

_____

Activity 12 | Document-Based Activity
The U.S. Response to the Holocaust

Writing a Document-Based Essay

HISTORICAL CONTEXT Germany's persecution of Jews began in the 1930s but grew worse after the start of World War II. In 1941 Adolph Hitler secretly ordered a campaign of mass murder to eliminate all Jews in Europe. U.S. officials received news of this plan in the summer of 1942 but were slow to react. Then, in January 1944, President Franklin Roosevelt created a War Refugee Board to help Jews escape from Nazi-controlled Europe. The board helped save over 200,000 Jews, but the Nazi genocide claimed over 6 million lives in total. Critics charge that the United States could have done much more to help the victims of the Holocaust.

TASK Using information from the documents and your knowledge of American history, write an essay in which you:

- Examine whether the United States could have further lessened the loss of life during the Holocaust, and if so, how.

- Discuss what factors limited the United States to saving the number of lives that it did.

Part B

DIRECTIONS Using the information from the documents provided and your knowledge of history, write a well-organized essay that includes an introduction, a body of several paragraphs, and a conclusion. Use examples from at least *four* documents in the body of the essay. Support your response with relevant facts, examples, and details. Include additional outside information.

GUIDELINES
In your essay, be sure to:

- Address all aspects of the **Task** by accurately analyzing and interpreting at least *four* documents.

- Incorporate information from the documents in the body of the essay.

- Incorporate relevant outside information.

- Support the theme with relevant facts, examples, and details.

- Use a logical and clear plan of organization.

- Introduce the theme by establishing a framework that is beyond a simple statement of the **Task** or **Historical Context**.

- Conclude the essay with a summation of the theme.

Activity 13

Document-Based Activity
The Korean War

Using Source Materials

HISTORICAL CONTEXT At the end of World War II the United States
and the Soviet Union divided Korea into two occupation zones. This
division became permanent when the two sides could not agree on a single
government for the country. The United States then set up the Republic of
Korea to govern the south, and the Soviets installed a Communist regime
in the north. After U.S. and Soviet troops withdrew, relations were tense
between the two Korean governments. In June 1950 North Korea invaded
South Korea. A year earlier, Communist forces had prevailed in the
Chinese Civil War. U.S. leaders did not want another Asian nation to fall
to communism, and so the United States quickly responded to the North
Korean invasion.

TASK Using information from the documents and your knowledge of
American history, answer the questions that follow each document in
Part A. Your answers to the questions will help you write the Part B essay.

Part A

DIRECTIONS Examine the following documents and answer the short-
answer questions that follow each document.

DOCUMENT 1

> It is possible that the South Koreans may themselves contain and repulse
> the attack and, if so, this is the best way. If, however, it appears that they
> cannot do so, then we believe that United States force should be used . . .
> To sit by while Korea is overrun by unprovoked armed attack would start a
> disastrous chain of events leading most probably to world war.
>
> —John Foster Dulles and John Allison
> Telegram to President Harry Truman, June 25, 1950

1. What did the writers of the telegram hope would happen?

_____

_____

2. What advice did they give to President Harry Truman, and why?

_____

Activity 13   Document-Based Activity

The Korean War

DOCUMENT 2

Before You Read The following word in the document below may be new
to you: *cessation*. You may want to use a dictionary to look it up.

The attack on the Republic of Korea . . . was a clear challenge to the basic
principles of the United Nations Charter . . . The Security Council of the
United Nations met, at the request of the United States, in New York at
two o'clock in the afternoon, Sunday, June 25th, eastern daylight time . . .
just 24 hours after the attack began.

At this meeting, the Security Council passed a resolution which called
for the immediate cessation of hostilities and for the withdrawal of the
invading troops to the thirty-eighth parallel, and which requested the
members of the United Nations to refrain from giving aid to the northern
aggressors and to assist in the execution of this resolution. The
representative of the Soviet Union to the Security Council stayed away
from the meetings, and the Soviet Government has refused to support the
Council's resolution . . .

Throughout Monday, June 26th, the invaders continued their attack with
no heed to the resolution of the Security Council of the United Nations.
Accordingly, in order to support the resolution, and on the unanimous
advice of our civil and military authorities, I ordered United States air and
sea forces to give the Korean Government troops cover and support.

On Tuesday, June 27th . . . the United Nations Security Council met
again and passed a second resolution recommending that members of the
United Nations furnish to the Republic of Korea such aid as might be
necessary to repel the attack . . . A number of member nations have offered
military support or other types of assistance for the United Nations action
to repel the aggressors in Korea.

—President Harry Truman
Address to Congress, July 19, 1950

---

1. Contrast the actions of the United States and the Soviet Union as described in the
   address.

   _____

   _____

2. According to the address, what were the consequences of these actions?

   _____

   _____

   _____

Activity 13   Document-Based Activity

The Korean War

DOCUMENT 3

Recent developments in Korea confront the world with a serious crisis. The Chinese Communist leaders have sent their troops from Manchuria to launch a strong and well-organized attack against the United Nations forces in North Korea. This has been done despite prolonged and earnest efforts to bring home to the Communist leaders of China the plain fact that neither the United Nations nor the United States has any aggressive intentions toward China. Because of the historic friendship between the people of the United States and China, it is particularly shocking to us to think that Chinese are being forced into battle against our troops in the United Nations command.

The Chinese attack was made in great force, and it still continues. It has resulted in the forced withdrawal of large parts of the United Nations command. The battlefield situation is uncertain at this time. We may suffer reverses as we have suffered them before. But the forces of the United Nations have no intention of abandoning their mission in Korea.

If the United Nations yields to the forces of aggression, no nation will be safe or secure. If aggression is successful in Korea, we can expect it to spread throughout Asia and Europe to this hemisphere. We are fighting in Korea for our own national security and survival.

We have committed ourselves to the cause of a just and peaceful world order through the United Nations. We stand by that commitment.

We shall meet the new situation in three ways.

We shall continue to work in the United Nations for concerted action to halt this aggression in Korea.

We shall intensify our efforts to help other free nations strengthen their defenses in order to meet the threat of aggression elsewhere.

We shall rapidly increase our own military strength.

—President Harry Truman
Press conference comments, November 30, 1950

1. How did the battlefield situation in Korea change in November 1950?

_____

_____

2. How do you think the new situation affected other nations around the world?

_____

_____

Document-Based Activity
The Korean War

DOCUMENT 4

Before You Read The following word in the document below may be new to you: *infiltration.* You may want to use a dictionary to look it up.

> The enemy made maximum use of his great manpower advantage for the infiltration and encirclement of our forces. They combined guerilla tactics with a shrewd use of modern weapons . . . They made the most of night attacks, in which assaults were launched to the blowing of bugles, and squads controlled by the shriek of whistles. An amazing number of Chinese and Koreans spoke a little English. These men would strip overcoats and parkas from our dead soldiers and try to make us believe they were friends. Others learned to yell "medic, medic" and trick us into revealing our positions . . .
>
> The original North Korean Army that struck southward on June twenty-fifth probably totaled close to one hundred and fifty thousand men. Even without air power and without sea power, they mauled us badly until the Inchon landing.
>
> Then the Chinese armies stepped in. The Chinese Peoples Liberation Army consists of five million men. But Far Eastern experts say that only two million of these are first-rate front-line troops . . .
>
> These forces are not only the best trained but also the best equipped in China . . . They seized many American bazookas, jeeps, trucks, and fieldpieces in Manchuria and they captured many American weapons from the Chinese Nationalists . . .
>
> Air power and artillery are not enough when you are vastly outnumbered in mountainous terrain. Even the marines, fully supported by air and equipped with the best American weapons, could not cope with the masses of howling, bugle-blowing Chinese. In the mountains of East Korea ill-equipped Chinese pushed the marines back by sheer weight of numbers.
>
> —Marguerite Higgins, newspaper correspondent in Korea
> *War in Korea: The Report of a Woman Combat Correspondent*

1. What was the primary advantage of the Communist forces fighting in Korea?

_____

_____

2. What tactics did the Communist troops use in Korea?

_____

_____

Activity 13

Document-Based Activity

The Korean War

DOCUMENT 5
Communist Advances and Military Threats in East Asia, November 1950

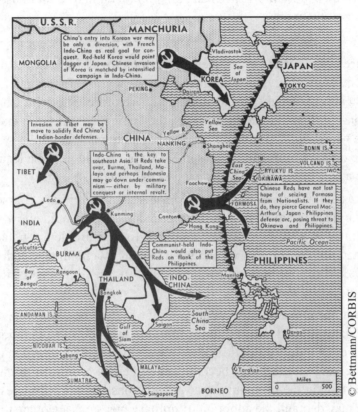

1. How did the mapmakers assess Chinese goals regarding Korea?

_____

_____

_____

2. How do you think this map influenced Americans during the Korean War?

_____

_____

_____

Activity 13

Document-Based Activity

The Korean War

DOCUMENT 6

Before You Read The following words in the document below may be
new to you: *armistice, heretofore, premise, attrition*. You may want to use
a dictionary to look them up.

> 6. Failure of the current armistice negotiations would indicate the desire of
> the enemy to prolong the hostilities in Korea, possibly for an indefinite
> period at approximately the same scale as heretofore. The Joint Chiefs of
> Staff consider that the measures which they now recommend in that
> premise would, in all probability, be sufficient to maintain military
> pressure on the Communist forces in Korea but would not be adequate to
> achieve a conclusive military decision in the Korean struggle.
>
> 7. The Joint Chiefs of Staff have considered other military courses of
> action for the attainment of a military decision which would allow
> achievement of a political settlement of the Korean problem satisfactory to
> the United States. They have concluded that any such military courses of
> action would require the employment of significant additional United
> States forces and means.
>
> 8. From the United States military point of view, the immobilization of
> United States ground, air, and naval forces in inconclusive operations in
> Korea over an indefinite period of time with the attendant attrition of
> manpower and materiel may become unacceptable. Moreover, it must be
> expected that, in the event armistice negotiations fail, United States public
> opinion may demand the adoption of military measures adequate to
> achieve a satisfactory military conclusion of the Korean struggle. The Joint
> Chiefs of Staff are aware of the implications involved in the intensification
> of military action in Korea on a greatly increased scale.
>
> —Omar Bradley, Chairman, Joint Chiefs of Staff
> NSC-118, Report for the Commander of UN Forces, November 9, 1951

1. What was the military situation in Korea at the time of this report?

_____

_____

2. What did Chairman Omar Bradley suggest might happen if the armistice negotiations
   failed?

_____

_____

Document-Based Activities

Activity 13

Document-Based Activity

The Korean War

DOCUMENT 7

Whatever the Communist attitude toward an armistice has been or now is, it is clear that their ability to increase their military capabilities in Korea lessens any willingness on their part to make concessions to obtain an armistice . . . Their increased capabilities [mean] that the United Nations Command is confronted with enemy forces, with good morale, numerically superior in strength, with adequate logistic support, and disposed in extremely well organized defensive positions in depth. A growing air potential including jet light bombers adds to these capabilities . . .

Current Restrictions on Military Operations

. . . c. *Operational Restrictions*:

(1) Except with approval of higher authority in Washington, UN forces will not cross Manchuria or USSR border of Korea.

(2) Air and offensive naval surface operations should not be conducted within 12 miles to seaward of the coasts of Manchuria or of the USSR on the Asiatic mainland.

(3) Aerial reconnaissance over all Korean territory, including coastal waters, is authorized up to, the Yalu River on the West Coast, but short of the Korean-Soviet international boundary on the East Coast.

(4) Only the President as Commander-in-Chief of the Armed Forces has authority to order or authorize preventive U.S. action against concentrations on the Chinese mainland.

(5) Employment of atomic weapons is authorized "only in the event our forces in that area would otherwise be faced with a military disaster", and upon approval of the President . . .

(7) Naval blockade will not be imposed against China.

—NSC-147
"Analysis of Possible Courses of Action in Korea," April 2, 1953

1. What advantages did the Communist forces have at the time of this report?

_____

_____

2. What do you think was the purpose of the restrictions leaders had placed on United Nations and U.S. forces?

_____

_____

Writing a Document-Based Essay

HISTORICAL CONTEXT At the end of World War II the United States and the Soviet Union divided Korea into two occupation zones. This division became permanent when the two sides could not agree on a single government for the country. The United States then set up the Republic of Korea to govern the south, and the Soviets installed a Communist regime in the north. After U.S. and Soviet troops withdrew, relations were tense between the two Korean governments. In June 1950 North Korea invaded South Korea. A year earlier, Communist forces had prevailed in the Chinese Civil War. U.S. leaders did not want another Asian nation to fall to communism, and so the United States quickly responded to the North Korean invasion.

TASK Using information from the documents and your knowledge of American history, write an essay in which you:

- Explain how the United States responded to the North Korean invasion of South Korea in 1950.

- Discuss the challenges that Americans faced during the Korean War.

Part B

DIRECTIONS Using the information from the documents provided and your knowledge of history, write a well-organized essay that includes an introduction, a body of several paragraphs, and a conclusion. In the body of the essay, use examples from at least *four* documents. Support your response with relevant facts, examples, and details. Include additional outside information.

GUIDELINES
In your essay, be sure to:

- Address all aspects of the **Task** by accurately analyzing and interpreting at least *four* documents.

- Incorporate information from the documents in the body of the essay.

- Incorporate relevant outside information.

- Support the theme with relevant facts, examples, and details.

- Use a logical and clear plan of organization.

- Introduce the theme by establishing a framework that is beyond a simple statement of the **Task** or **Historical Context**.

- Conclude the essay with a summation of the theme.

Activity 14

Document-Based Activity

The Civil Rights Movement

Using Source Materials

HISTORICAL CONTEXT The Civil Rights Act of 1964 and the Voting Rights Act of 1965 were major victories for the civil rights movement. African Americans, however, continued to endure poverty and prejudice. Frustration with this lingering inequality exploded in a series of urban riots in 1965–1968. As young African Americans began to reject nonviolence and join revolutionary groups such as the Black Panthers, a rift grew between whites and blacks. The murder of Martin Luther King Jr. in 1968 further weakened the movement and silenced its most inspiring leader.

TASK Using information from the documents and your knowledge of American history, answer the questions that follow each document in Part A. Your answers to the questions will help you write the Part B essay.

Part A

DIRECTIONS Examine the following documents and answer the short-answer questions that follow each document.

DOCUMENT 1

> We had seen how the police attacked the Watts community [in Los Angeles] after causing the trouble in the first place. We had seen Martin Luther King come to Watts in an effort to calm the people, and we had seen his philosophy of nonviolence rejected. Black people had been taught nonviolence . . . What good, however, was nonviolence when the police were determined to rule by force? . . . We recognized that the rising consciousness of Black people was almost at the point of explosion.
>
> —Huey P. Newton, co-founder of the Black Panther Party
> *Revolutionary Suicide*, 1973

1. Who did Huey Newton believe was responsible for starting the Watts riots in 1965?

_____

_____

2. How did Newton assess nonviolence as a strategy for the civil rights movement?

_____

_____

Document-Based Activities

DOCUMENT 2

Before You Read The following word in the second document below may
be new to you: *manifest*. You may want to use a dictionary to look it up.

> Dr. King's marches in Chicago were usually made up of movement people.
> This march was community people. These people had not attended any
> workshops on nonviolence, they had not listened to any lectures on loving
> your fellow man and all. They were just people who were angry about
> what was happening and wanted to do something. When they all decided to
> go on this march, and people started to throw bricks and bottles at us, a
> couple of people caught the bricks and threw them back.
>
> > —Linda Bryant Hall, Congress of Racial Equality member
> > Description of the 1966 civil rights march in Chicago
>
> I felt really good about the blacks catching the missiles and throwing them
> back, because it sorely indicated to the whole world that nonviolence had
> worked in the South but it wasn't about to really work in the North.
>
> After Dr. King left the city in late August of 1966, having failed really in
> Chicago, we began to notice a wider split between the blacks and the
> whites in the civil rights movement. As long as Dr. King was here, that was
> sort of held at bay, out of respect for him. But after he left, it really began
> to manifest itself to the point where blacks literally asked whites to leave
> the movement and to leave meetings. But, you see, that had really started
> back around 1964 because of the preachings of Malcolm X. A lot of blacks
> in the civil rights movement, although they did not become Muslims, they
> really believed in Malcolm X and Malcolm's preaching. Inasmuch as some
> people already had those kind of inclinations, it manifested itself in a huge
> way in the fall of '66 and later.
>
> > —Bob Lucas, Chicago Congress of Racial Equality president

1. What did some civil rights marchers in Chicago do when people threw objects at
   them? What did their response demonstrate?

   _____

   _____

   _____

2. How, according to Bob Lucas, did the civil rights movement change in 1966?

   _____

   _____

Document-Based Activity
The Civil Rights Movement

DOCUMENT 3
Newark, New Jersey, 1967

© Bettmann/CORBIS

1. This photograph was taken after two nights of rioting during a five-day disturbance in Newark. What do you notice about the people and the neighborhood shown?

_____

_____

_____

2. How do you think supporters and opponents of the civil rights movement might have interpreted this photograph differently?

_____

_____

_____

_____

Activity 14

Document-Based Activity

The Civil Rights Movement

DOCUMENT 4

Before You Read The following words in the document below may be new to you: *permeated, polarization, capitulation, condones.* You may want to use a dictionary to look them up.

The summer of 1967 again brought racial disorders to American cities, and with them shock, fear and bewilderment to the nation . . .

On July 28, 1967, the President of the United States established this Commission and directed us to answer three basic questions: What happened? Why did it happen? What can be done to prevent it from happening again? . . .

This is our basic conclusion: *Our nation is moving toward two societies, one black, one white—separate and unequal.*

Reaction to last summer's disorders has quickened the movement and deepened the division. Discrimination and segregation have long permeated much of American life; they now threaten the future of every American. The deepening racial division is not inevitable. The movement apart can be reversed. Choice is still possible. Our principle task is to define that choice and to press for a national resolution.

To pursue the present course will involve the continuing polarization of the American community and, ultimately, the destruction of basic democratic values. The alternative is not blind repression or capitulation to lawlessness. It is the realization of common opportunities for all within a single society . . .

Segregation and poverty have created in the racial ghetto a destructive environment totally unknown to most white Americans.

What white Americans have never fully understood—but what the Negro can never forget—is that the white society is deeply implicated in the ghetto. White institutions created it, white institutions maintain it, and white society condones it . . .

—Report of the National Advisory Commission on Civil Disorders, 1968

---

1. According to the commission, what conditions led to the race riots of 1967?

_____

_____

2. What did the commission predict would happen if changes were not made?

_____

_____

Document-Based Activities

Activity 14

Document-Based Activity
The Civil Rights Movement

DOCUMENT 5

Before You Read The following words in the document below may be
new to you: *facile*, *eviscerated*, *demonic*. You may want to use a dictionary
to look them up.

> Over the past two years . . . as I have called for radical departures from the
> destruction of Vietnam, many persons have questioned me about the
> wisdom of my path . . . Peace and civil rights don't mix, they say . . .
>
> There is at the onset a very obvious and almost facile connection
> between the war in Vietnam and the struggle I, and others, have been
> waging in America. A few years ago there was a shining moment in that
> struggle. It seemed as if there was a real promise of hope for the poor—
> both black and white—through the [federal] Poverty Program. Then came
> the build-up in Vietnam, and I watched the program broken and
> eviscerated as if it were some idle political plaything of a society gone mad
> on war, and I knew that America would never invest the necessary funds or
> energies in rehabilitation of its poor so long as Vietnam continued to draw
> men and skills and money like some demonic, destructive suction tube . . .
>
> Perhaps the more tragic recognition of reality took place when it became
> clear to me that the war was doing far more than devastating the hopes of
> the poor at home. It was sending their sons and their brothers and their
> husbands to fight and to die in extraordinarily high proportions relative to
> the rest of the population. We were taking the young black men who had
> been crippled by our society and sending them 8000 miles away to
> guarantee liberties in Southeast Asia which they had not found in
> Southwest Georgia and East Harlem. So we have been repeatedly faced
> with the cruel irony of watching Negro and white boys on TV screens as
> they kill and die together for a nation that has been unable to seat them
> together in the same schools.
>
> —Martin Luther King Jr., "Beyond Vietnam," 1967

1. Why did Martin Luther King Jr. view the war in Vietnam as a setback for the civil
   rights movement?

   _____

   _____

2. What irony did King see in the American war effort in Vietnam?

   _____

   _____

Activity 14   Document-Based Activity
                                    ## The Civil Rights Movement

DOCUMENT 6

Before You Read The following word in the document below may be new
to you: *punitive.* You may want to use a dictionary to look it up.

I'll never forget, I was standing, at one point, next to a reporter from the
New York Times, and he was obviously saddened by Dr. King's death. He
was an important writer for the *Times*. Recalling an article on Vietnam and
Dr. King, an editorial very critical and highly misleading which helped to
fan the flames of discontent with Martin, painting him as unpatriotic,
making people quite angry with him and the movement, I could not help
but tell him that this grievous moment was in part the result of a climate of
hate and distortion that the *New York Times* and other papers had helped
create. In particular the way the *Washington Post* wrote its editorial on Dr.
King and Vietnam. It was misleading. It was punitive. It was a great
disservice to a great cause.

—Harry Belafonte, singer and actor
Recollection of Martin Luther King Jr.'s funeral, 1968

The murder of King changed the whole dynamic of the country. That is
probably the single most significant event in terms of how the Panthers
were perceived by the black community. Because once King was
murdered, in April '68, that kind of ended any public commitment to
nonviolent change. It was like, "Well, we tried that, and that's what
happened." So even though there were many people, and many black
people, who thought nonviolent change was a good thing and the best
thing, nobody came out publicly and supported it. Because even nonviolent
change was violently rejected. So it's like the Panthers were all of a sudden
thrust into the forefront of being the alternative, and maybe weren't quite
anticipating as much attention as they got—neither the media attention nor
the police repression. 'Cause they sort of went hand in hand.

—Kathleen Neal Cleaver
Wife of Eldridge Cleaver, Black Panther Party minister of information

1. How did Harry Belafonte assess the press coverage of Martin Luther King Jr.?

_____

_____

2. According to Mrs. Cleaver, how did King's death change the civil rights movement?

_____

_____

_____

Activity 14

Document-Based Activity

The Civil Rights Movement

DOCUMENT 7

Before You Read The following words in the document below may be
new to you: *vigilante*, *propagation*, *propensity*. You may want to use a
dictionary to look them up.

COINTELPRO [a series of covert, federal counterintelligence programs]
began in 1956 . . . It ended in 1971 with the threat of public exposure. In
the intervening 15 years, the Bureau [FBI] conducted a sophisticated
vigilante operation aimed squarely at preventing the exercise of First
Amendment rights of speech and association, on the theory that preventing
the growth of dangerous groups and the propagation of dangerous ideas
would protect the national security and deter violence . . .

The Black Nationalist COINTELPRO and the racial intelligence
investigation section were set up at about the same time in 1967.

Prior to that time, the Division's investigations of "Negro matters" was
limited . . . However, the long, hot summer of 1967 led to intense pressure
on the Bureau to do something to contain the problem . . .

The originating letter was sent out to twenty-three field offices on
August 25, 1967, describing the program's purpose as: ". . . to expose,
disrupt, misdirect, discredit, or otherwise neutralize the activities of black
nationalist, hate-type organizations and groupings, their leadership . . . and
to counter their propensity for violence and civil disorder." . . .

From December 1963 until his death in 1968, Martin Luther King, Jr.
was the target of an intensive campaign by the Federal Bureau of
Investigation to "neutralize" him as an effective civil rights leader . . .

By July 1969, the Black Panthers had become the primary focus of the
program, and was ultimately the target of 233 of the total 295 authorized
"Black Nationalist" COINTELPRO actions.

—U.S. Senate, Final Report of the Select Committee to Study
Governmental Operations with Respect to Intelligence Activities, 1976

1. How and why did the FBI violate the Constitution with its COINTELPRO program?

_____

_____

2. Why do you think the FBI targeted Martin Luther King Jr. and the Black Panthers?

_____

_____

Activity 14

Document-Based Activity
The Civil Rights Movement

Writing a Document-Based Essay

HISTORICAL CONTEXT The Civil Rights Act of 1964 and the Voting Rights Act of 1965 were major victories for the civil rights movement. African Americans, however, continued to endure poverty and prejudice. Frustration with this lingering inequality exploded in a series of urban riots in 1965–1968. As young African Americans began to reject nonviolence and join revolutionary groups such as the Black Panthers, a rift grew between whites and blacks. The murder of Martin Luther King Jr. in 1968 further weakened the movement and silenced its most inspiring leader.

TASK Using information from the documents and your knowledge of American history, write an essay in which you:

- Discuss the changing character of the civil rights movement between 1965 and 1970.

- Describe the challenges civil rights supporters faced in the late 1960s.

Part B

DIRECTIONS Using the information from the documents provided and your knowledge of American history, write a well-organized essay that includes an introduction, a body of several paragraphs, and a conclusion. In the body of the essay, use examples from at least *four* documents. Support your response with relevant facts, examples, and details. Include additional outside information.

GUIDELINES
In your essay, be sure to:

- Address all aspects of the **Task** by accurately analyzing and interpreting at least *four* documents.

- Incorporate information from the documents in the body of the essay.

- Incorporate relevant outside information.

- Support the theme with relevant facts, examples, and details.

- Use a logical and clear plan of organization.

- Introduce the theme by establishing a framework that is beyond a simple statement of the **Task** or **Historical Context**.

- Conclude the essay with a summation of the theme.

Activity 15   Document-Based Activity

The Vietnam War

Using Source Materials

HISTORICAL CONTEXT In 1954 Vietnamese nationalists ended French colonial rule in Southeast Asia. A Communist government then formed in North Vietnam, while a non-Communist regime, supported by the United States, governed the South. Vietnamese Communists created a guerrilla army, the Vietcong, to overthrow the pro-American government in the South. By 1965 South Vietnam neared collapse. President Lyndon Johnson sent U.S. troops to fight the Vietcong, but the war became a bloody stalemate. As U.S. losses mounted, Americans grew critical of the war effort and their own government.

TASK Using information from the documents and your knowledge of American history, answer the questions that follow each document in Part A. Your answers to the questions will help you write the Part B essay.

Part A

DIRECTIONS Examine the following documents and answer the short-answer questions that follow each document.

DOCUMENT 1

> . . . the Congress approves and supports the determination of the President, as Commander in Chief, to take all necessary measures to repel any armed attack against the forces of the United States and to prevent further aggression . . . Consonant with the Constitution . . . and in accordance with its obligations under the Southeast Asia Collective Defense Treaty, the United States is, therefore, prepared, as the President determines, to take all necessary steps, including the use of armed force, to assist any member or protocol state of the Southeast Asia Collective Defense Treaty . . .
>
> —The Tonkin Gulf Resolution, 1964

1. What powers did the president gain with this resolution?

_____

2. How did this resolution affect America's likelihood of becoming involved in a war?

_____

_____

DOCUMENT 2

Before You Read The following word in the document below may be new
to you: *appeaser*. You may want to use a dictionary to look it up.

> "I knew from the start . . . that I was bound to be crucified either way I
> moved. If I left the woman I really loved—the Great Society—in order to
> get involved with that . . . war on the other side of the world, then I would
> lose everything at home. All my programs. All my hopes to feed the
> hungry and shelter the homeless. All my dreams to provide education and
> medical care to the browns and the blacks and the lame and the poor. But if
> I left that war and let the Communists take over South Vietnam, then I
> would be seen as a coward and my nation would be seen as an appeaser
> and we would both find it impossible to accomplish anything for anybody
> anywhere on the entire globe . . .
>
> Once the war began, then all those conservatives in the Congress would
> use it as a weapon against the Great Society. You see, they'd never wanted
> to help the poor or the Negroes in the first place. But they were having a
> hard time figuring out how to make their opposition sound noble in a time
> of great prosperity. But the war. Oh, they'd use it to say they were against
> my programs, not because they were against the poor . . . but because the
> war had to come first. First we had to beat those godless Communists, and
> then we could worry about the homeless Americans . . .
>
> And I knew that if we let Communist aggression succeed in taking over
> South Vietnam, there would follow in this country an endless national
> debate—a mean and destructive debate—that would shatter my presidency,
> kill my Administration, and damage our democracy . . . "
>
> —President Lyndon B. Johnson, as told to historian Doris Kearns
> "Who *Was* Lyndon Baines Johnson?" *Atlantic Monthly*, July 1976

1. What did President Lyndon B. Johnson believe were the consequences of getting
   involved in the war in Vietnam?

   _____

   _____

2. What did President Johnson believe were the consequences of not getting involved in
   the war in Vietnam?

   _____

   _____

Document-Based Activities

DOCUMENT 3

Before You Read The following word in the document below may be new
to you: *partisanship*. You may want to use a dictionary to look it up.

For 37 years in the service of our Nation, first as a Congressman, as a
Senator, and as Vice President, and now as your President, I have put the
unity of the people first. I have put it ahead of any divisive partisanship.

And in these times as in times before, it is true that a house divided
against itself by the spirit of faction, of party, of region, of religion, of race,
is a house that cannot stand.

There is division in the American house now. There is divisiveness
among us all tonight. And holding the trust that is mine, as President of all
the people, I cannot disregard the peril to the progress of the American
people and the hope and the prospect of peace for all peoples.

So, I would ask all Americans, whatever their personal interests or
concern, to guard against divisiveness and all its ugly consequences . . .

Believing this as I do, I have concluded that I should not permit the
Presidency to become involved in the partisan divisions that are developing
in this political year.

With America's sons in the fields far away, with America's future under
challenge right here at home, with our hopes and the world's hopes for
peace in the balance every day, I do not believe that I should devote an
hour or a day of my time to any personal partisan causes or to any duties
other than the awesome duties of this office—the Presidency of your
country.

Accordingly, I shall not seek, and I will not accept, the nomination of
my party for another term as your President.

—President Lyndon B. Johnson
"Address to the Nation," March 31, 1968

---

1. In his speech, how did President Lyndon B. Johnson describe the political climate in
   the United States?

   _____

   _____

2. What major decision did President Johnson reveal? Why do you think he made that
   decision?

   _____

   _____

Activity 15   Document-Based Activity

The Vietnam War

DOCUMENT 4

I believe that one of the reasons for the deep division about Vietnam is that many Americans have lost confidence in what their Government has told them about our policy. The American people cannot and should not be asked to support a policy which involves the overriding issues of war and peace unless they know the truth about that policy . . .

At the time we launched our search for peace I recognized we might not succeed in bringing an end to the war through negotiation. I, therefore, put into effect another plan to bring peace—a plan which will bring the war to an end regardless of what happens on the negotiating front . . .

. . . we shall furnish military and economic assistance when requested in accordance with our treaty commitments. But we shall look to the nation directly threatened to assume the primary responsibility of providing the manpower for its defense . . .

The defense of freedom is everybody's business—not just America's business. And it is particularly the responsibility of the people whose freedom is threatened. In the previous administration, we Americanized the war in Vietnam. In this administration, we are Vietnamizing the search for peace . . .

After 5 years of Americans going into Vietnam, we are finally bringing American men home. By December 15, over 60,000 men will have been withdrawn from South Vietnam . . .

The South Vietnamese have continued to gain in strength. As a result they have been able to take over combat responsibilities from our American troops . . .

I pledged in my campaign for the Presidency to end the war in a way that we could win the peace. I have initiated a plan of action which will enable me to keep that pledge.

—President Richard Nixon
"Address to the Nation," November 3, 1969

1. What new plan did President Richard Nixon announce regarding Vietnam?

_____

_____

2. Why do you think President Nixon initiated this plan?

_____

_____

DOCUMENT 5
Washington, D.C., May 9, 1970

© JP Laffont/Sygma/CORBIS

1. Where in Washington, D.C., did this antiwar protest take place? Why do you think the protesters chose this location?

_____

_____

_____

2. What does the sign indicate about the protesters' opinion of President Richard Nixon?

_____

_____

_____

Activity 15   Document-Based Activity

The Vietnam War

DOCUMENT 6

> The Nixon Administration, alarmed by what it regards as a rising tide of radical extremism, is planning to step up surveillance of militant left-wing groups and individuals.
>
> The objective, according to White House officials, is to find out who the potential bomb planters and snipers may be before they endanger others.
>
> Preparations for expanding and improving the domestic intelligence apparatus—informers, undercover agents, wiretaps—were disclosed in a series of interviews with key officials, who requested anonymity.
>
> According to these officials, President Nixon is disturbed by the rash of bombings and bomb scares, courtroom disruptions and reports of small but growing numbers of young people who feel alienated from the American system . . .
>
> The official view is that extreme radicals cannot be won over with welfare, electoral or draft reforms or by White House appeals . . . Accordingly, the Administration sees its prime responsibility as protecting the innocent from "revolutionary terrorism." The President said last month, when he asked Congress for broader Federal jurisdiction and stiffer penalties in bombing cases, that they were the work of "young criminals posturing as romantic revolutionaries" . . .
>
> The White House is aware of the political sensitivity of domestic intelligence gathering, which one aide described as "hangups in the question of snooping" . . .
>
> He argued that it would, in fact, increase safeguards of the civil liberties of individuals to have a greater awareness of which members of society posed a threat.
>
> —James Naughton, "U.S. to Tighten Surveillance of Radicals"
> *The New York Times*, April 12, 1970

1. Why do you think the Nixon administration developed the plan described in the article?

_____

_____

2. What were the potential dangers of the plan?

_____

_____

Activity 15

Document-Based Activity

The Vietnam War

DOCUMENT 7

SEC. 2. (a) It is the purpose of this joint resolution to fulfill the intent of the framers of the Constitution of the United States and insure that the collective judgment of both the Congress and the President will apply to the introduction of United States Armed Forces into hostilities, or into situations where imminent involvement in hostilities is clearly indicated by the circumstances, and to the continued use of such forces in hostilities or in such situations . . .

SEC. 3. The President in every possible instance shall consult with Congress before introducing United States Armed Forces into hostilities or into situation where imminent involvement in hostilities is clearly indicated by the circumstances, and after every such introduction shall consult regularly with the Congress until United States Armed Forces are no longer engaged in hostilities or have been removed from such situations . . .

SEC. 5. . . . (b) Within sixty calendar days after a report is submitted or is required to be submitted . . . whichever is earlier, the President shall terminate any use of United States Armed Forces with respect to which such report was submitted . . . unless the Congress (1) has declared war or has enacted a specific authorization for such use of United States Armed Forces, (2) has extended by law such sixty-day period, or (3) is physically unable to meet as a result of an armed attack upon the United States . . .

(c) Notwithstanding subsection (b), at any time that United States Armed Forces are engaged in hostilities outside the territory of the United States, its possessions and territories without a declaration of war or specific statutory authorization, such forces shall be removed by the President if the Congress so directs by concurrent resolution.

—War Powers Resolution, 1973

1. How did the War Powers Resolution affect presidential power?

_____

_____

2. How do you think the Vietnam War influenced the passage of this resolution by Congress?

_____

_____

Activity 15   Document-Based Activity

Writing a Document-Based Essay

HISTORICAL CONTEXT In 1954 Vietnamese nationalists ended French colonial rule in Southeast Asia. A Communist government then formed in North Vietnam, while a non-Communist regime, supported by the United States, governed the South. Vietnamese Communists created a guerrilla army, the Vietcong, to overthrow the pro-American government in the South. By 1965 South Vietnam neared collapse. President Lyndon Johnson sent U.S. troops to fight the Vietcong, but the war became a bloody stalemate. As U.S. losses mounted, Americans grew critical of the war effort and their own government.

TASK Using information from the documents and your knowledge of American history, write an essay in which you:

- Explain how the Vietnam War affected the presidencies of Lyndon Johnson and Richard Nixon.

- Describe how presidential power changed during the Vietnam War.

Part B

DIRECTIONS Using the information from the documents provided and your knowledge of American history, write a well-organized essay that includes an introduction, a body of several paragraphs, and a conclusion. In the body of the essay, use examples from at least *four* documents. Support your response with relevant facts, examples, and details. Include additional outside information.

GUIDELINES
In your essay, be sure to:

- Address all aspects of the **Task** by accurately analyzing and interpreting at least *four* documents.

- Incorporate information from the documents in the body of the essay.

- Incorporate relevant outside information.

- Support the theme with relevant facts, examples, and details.

- Use a logical and clear plan of organization.

- Introduce the theme by establishing a framework that is beyond a simple statement of the **Task** or **Historical Context**.

- Conclude the essay with a summation of the theme.

Activity 16

Document-Based Activity

The Reagan Era

Using Source Materials

HISTORICAL CONTEXT Soon after taking office in 1981, President Ronald Reagan initiated a massive military build-up. Vowing to resist global communism, the president sent U.S. troops into Grenada and supported the Contra rebels in Nicaragua. President Reagan also took action against world terrorism. His administration, however, endured foreign policy setbacks. The Iran-Contra affair sparked severe criticism of the president. Rebounding from that scandal, Reagan worked effectively to improve relations with the Soviet Union during his last two years in office.

TASK Using information from the documents and your knowledge of American history, answer the questions that follow each document in Part A. Your answers to the questions will help you write the Part B essay.

Part A

DIRECTIONS Examine the following documents and answer the short-answer questions that follow each document.

DOCUMENT 1

> . . . the Soviet leaders have openly and publicly declared that the only morality they recognize is that which will further their cause, which is world revolution . . . Yes, let us pray for the salvation of all of those who live in that totalitarian darkness—pray they will discover the joy of knowing God. But until they do, let us be aware that while they preach the supremacy of the state . . . and predict its eventual domination of all peoples on the Earth, they are the focus of evil in the modern world.
>
> —President Ronald Reagan
> Address to the National Association of Evangelicals, March 8, 1983

1. How did President Ronald Reagan describe the Soviet Union in his address?

_____

_____

2. What foreign policy goals did President Reagan allude to in this document?

_____

Activity 16

Document-Based Activity

The Reagan Era

DOCUMENT 2

For 20 years the Soviet Union has been accumulating enormous military might . . . During the past decade and a half, the Soviets have built up a massive arsenal of new strategic nuclear weapons—weapons that can strike directly at the United States . . .

As the Soviets have increased their military power, they've been emboldened to extend that power. They're spreading their military influence in ways that can directly challenge our vital interests . . .

When I took office in January 1981, I was appalled by what I found: American planes that couldn't fly and American ships that couldn't sail for lack of spare parts and trained personnel and insufficient fuel and ammunition for essential training . . .

We had to move immediately to improve the basic readiness and staying power of our conventional forces, so they could meet—and therefore help deter—a crisis. We had to make up for lost years of investment by moving forward with a long-term plan to prepare our forces to counter the military capabilities our adversaries were developing for the future . . .

The calls for cutting back the defense budget come in nice, simple arithmetic. They're the same kind of talk that led the democracies to neglect their defenses in the 1930's and invited . . . World War II . . .

This is why I'm speaking to you tonight to urge you to tell your Senators and Congressmen that you know we must continue to restore our military strength. If we stop in midstream, we will send a signal of decline . . . to friends and adversaries alike . . . It's up to us, in our time, to choose and choose wisely between the hard but necessary task of preserving peace and freedom and the temptation to ignore our duty and blindly hope for the best while the enemies of freedom grow stronger day by day.

—President Ronald Reagan
Address to the nation, March 23, 1983

1. According to the address, what did President Ronald Reagan want to do with the U.S. military?

   _____

   _____

2. What obstacles did President Reagan seek to overcome with this address?

   _____

   _____

Document-Based Activities

Activity 16

Document-Based Activity

The Reagan Era

DOCUMENT 3

Meanwhile, on Grenada the fighting continued all day long . . .

In the first twenty-four hours we took about 560 Cuban prisoners, plus several thousand Grenadian troops. It was evident that the people of Grenada *welcomed* the combined U.S. and Caribbean forces, recognizing them as liberators from a frightening, oppressive regime . . .

Even though the number was relatively small, there *were* casualties: 18 from the U.S. forces were killed and 116 wounded; Grenadian casualties included 45 killed and 337 wounded; and of the almost 800 Cubans, 29 were killed and 59 wounded . . .

Within days of the event U.S. public opinion polls showed that the overwhelming majority of the American people agreed that President Reagan had done the right thing. A bipartisan congressional delegation visited Grenada shortly after the rescue, and virtually all of the congressmen—including some of the Democrats who had been most critical—returned to say that they had talked to the Grenadian people and seen the warehouses filled with Cuban weapons, and they now agreed with the president.

After ten days had passed I urged that the captured files be carefully and systematically reviewed, along with the weapons and facilities used for the subversive training. We had a unique opportunity: Grenada was the first country where a communist regime had been toppled. That meant there had to be a rich vein of knowledge and insight to be mined by carefully analyzing the methods that had been used to consolidate power internally and the techniques of subversive cooperation with Cuba and the Soviet bloc.

—Constantine C. Menges
Special Assistant to the President for National Security Affairs
Describing the U.S. invasion of Grenada in October 1983

1. In what ways was the invasion of Grenada a significant Cold War event?

_____

_____

2. How do you think the invasion affected President Ronald Reagan's popularity?

_____

_____

_____

DOCUMENT 4
U.S. Marine Headquarters
Beirut, Lebanon, October 23, 1983

© Bettmann/CORBIS

1. What appears to have happened at the U.S. Marine headquarters building in Beirut?

_____

_____

_____

2. How do you think photographs like this one influenced American opinions about the use of U.S. troops as a peacekeeping force in Lebanon?

_____

_____

_____

Activity 16   Document-Based Activity

The Reagan Era

DOCUMENT 5

Before You Read The following words in the document below may be
new to you: *emphatically, perpetrated.* You may want to use a dictionary
to look them up.

President Reagan spoke on national television from the Oval Office at 9:00
P.M. on April 14, 1986. He announced that at seven o'clock that evening,
"Air and naval forces of the United States launched a series of strikes
against the headquarters, terrorist facilities and military assets that support
Muammar Qadhafi's subversive activities" . . .

The next morning, I went over to see the president. I congratulated him
on his tough decision. He felt, and I agreed, that we had emphatically put
down a marker that the United States was ready and able to take military
action against states that perpetrated terrorism . . .

The public response in the United States and Europe supported the
president's actions. His standing in public opinion polls soared. That made
an impact on congressional critics. More important, Qaddafi, after
twitching feverishly with a flurry of vengeful responses, quieted down and
retreated into the desert. The Europeans, more alert now to the dangers
posed to them by Libya, alarmed at the use of force by the United States,
and anxious to show cooperation with a popular U.S. action, took action of
their own. We had finally gotten their attention. They forced drastic
personnel reductions in the Libyan people's bureaus, and the activities of
those remaining were restricted and watched. This action alone
significantly curbed Qaddafi's terrorist capacities.

—George Shultz, Secretary of State
Describing the U.S. bombing of Libya in April 1986

1. According to this document, why did President Ronald Reagan order military strikes
   against Libya?

   _____

   _____

   _____

2. How did other nations respond to the United States' actions against Libya?

   _____

   _____

   _____

Activity 16   Document-Based Activity

The Reagan Era

DOCUMENT 6

Before You Read The following words in the document below may be
new to you: *proscriptions*, *paramilitary*, *Contras*, *adversaries*, *illicit*. You
may want to use a dictionary to look them up.

The United States simultaneously pursued two contradictory foreign
policies—a public one and a secret one:

The public policy was not to make any concessions for the release of
hostages lest such concessions encourage more hostage-taking. At the
same time, the United States was secretly trading weapons to get the
hostages back.

The public policy was to ban arms shipments to Iran and to exhort other
Governments to observe this embargo. At the same time, the United States
was secretly selling sophisticated missiles to Iran and promising more . . .

The public policy was to observe the "letter and spirit" of the Boland
Amendment's proscriptions against military or paramilitary assistance to
the Contras. At the same time, the NSC staff was secretly assuming
direction and funding of the Contras' military effort . . .

These contradictions in policy inevitably resulted in policy failure:

The United States armed Iran, including its most radical elements, but
attained neither a new relationship with that hostile regime nor a reduction
in the number of American hostages . . .

The United States opened itself to blackmail by adversaries who might
reveal the secret arms sales and who . . . threatened to kill the hostages if
the sales stopped . . .

The United States sought illicit funding for the Contras through profits
from the secret arms sales, but a substantial portion of those profits ended
up in the . . . bank accounts of the private individuals executing the sales.

—*Report of the Congressional Committees Investigating the
Iran-Contra Affair*, 1988

---

1. How did the United States violate its own stated foreign policies?

_____

_____

2. What were the results of the secret U.S. policies regarding Iran and Nicaragua?

_____

_____

Activity 16   Document-Based Activity

The Reagan Era

DOCUMENT 7

Before You Read The following word in the document below may be new
to you: *verification*. You may want to use a dictionary to look it up.

Ronald W. Reagan, President of the United States of America, and Mikhail
S. Gorbachev, General Secretary of the Central Committee of the
Communist Party of the Soviet Union, met in Washington on December 7-
10, 1987 . . .

The President and the General Secretary affirmed the fundamental
importance of their meetings in Geneva and Reykjavik, which laid the
basis for concrete steps in a process intended to improve strategic stability
and reduce the risk of conflict . . . They are determined to prevent any war
between the United States and the Soviet Union, whether nuclear or
conventional. They will not seek to achieve military superiority.

The two leaders recognized the special responsibility of the United
States and the Soviet Union to search for realistic ways to prevent
confrontation and to promote a more sustainable and stable relationship
between their countries. To this end, they agreed to intensify dialogue and
to encourage emerging trends toward constructive cooperation in all areas
of their relations . . .

The INF Treaty

The two leaders signed the Treaty between the United States of America
and the Union of Soviet Socialistic Republics on the Elimination of Their
Intermediate-Range and Shorter-Range Missiles. This treaty is historic
both for its objective—the complete elimination of an entire class of U.S.
and Soviet nuclear arms—and for the innovative character and scope of its
verification provisions. This mutual accomplishment makes a vital
contribution to greater stability.

—Joint Statement on the Soviet-United States Summit Meeting
December 10, 1987

---

1. Why was the treaty signed by President Ronald Reagan and General Secretary
   Mikhail Gorbachev significant?

   _____

   _____

2. How does the tone of this document differ from the tone of Documents 1 and 2?

   _____

   _____

Writing a Document-Based Essay

HISTORICAL CONTEXT Soon after taking office in 1981, President Ronald Reagan initiated a massive military build-up. Vowing to resist global communism, the president sent U.S. troops into Grenada and supported the Contra rebels in Nicaragua. President Reagan also took action against world terrorism. His administration, however, endured foreign policy setbacks. The Iran-Contra affair sparked severe criticism of the president. Rebounding from that scandal, Reagan worked effectively to improve relations with the Soviet Union during his last two years in office.

TASK Using information from the documents and your knowledge of American history, write an essay in which you:

- Describe the major foreign policy goals of the Reagan administration.

- Discuss the important U.S. foreign policy successes and failures during the Reagan presidency.

Part B

DIRECTIONS Using the information from the documents provided and your knowledge of American history, write a well-organized essay that includes an introduction, a body of several paragraphs, and a conclusion. In the body of the essay, use examples from at least *four* documents. Support your response with relevant facts, examples, and details. Include additional outside information.

GUIDELINES
In your essay, be sure to:

- Address all aspects of the **Task** by accurately analyzing and interpreting at least *four* documents.

- Incorporate information from the documents in the body of the essay.

- Incorporate relevant outside information.

- Support the theme with relevant facts, examples, and details.

- Use a logical and clear plan of organization.

- Introduce the theme by establishing a framework that is beyond a simple statement of the **Task** or **Historical Context**.

- Conclude the essay with a summation of the theme.

Activity 17

Document-Based Activity

The United States in Recent Times

Using Source Materials

HISTORICAL CONTEXT On September 11, 2001, terrorists hijacked four passenger airliners. They piloted two of the jets into the twin towers of the World Trade Center in New York. Hijackers flew another airliner into the Pentagon building in Washington, D.C. Passengers stormed the cockpit of the fourth jet, causing it to crash in a field in Pennsylvania. The 9/11 attacks claimed nearly 3,000 lives and shocked the nation. President George W. Bush vowed to punish those responsible for the tragedy. The United States then launched a sweeping campaign against terrorism.

TASK Using information from the documents and your knowledge of American history, answer the questions that follow each document in Part A. Your answers to the questions will help you write the Part B essay.

Part A

DIRECTIONS Examine the following documents and answer the short-answer questions that follow each document.

DOCUMENT 1

> Beginning on September 11, Immigration and Naturalization Service [INS] agents working in cooperation with the FBI began arresting individuals for immigration violations whom they encountered while following up leads in the FBI's investigation of the 9/11 attacks. Eventually, 768 aliens were arrested as "special interest" detainees . . . Attorney General John Ashcroft told us that he saw his job in directing this effort as "risk minimization," both to find out who had committed the attacks and to prevent a subsequent attack.
>
> —*The 9/11 Commission Report*

1. What action did the INS and FBI take in response to the 9/11 terrorist attacks?

_____

_____

2. What was the goal of these efforts?

_____

_____

Activity 17

Document-Based Activity

The United States in Recent Times

DOCUMENT 2

Before You Read The following word in the document below may be new to you: *staunch*. You may want to use a dictionary to look it up.

Good afternoon. On my orders, the United States military has begun strikes against al Qaeda terrorist training camps and military installations of the Taliban regime in Afghanistan. These carefully targeted actions are designed to disrupt the use of Afghanistan as a terrorist base of operations, and to attack the military capability of the Taliban regime.

We are joined in this operation by our staunch friend, Great Britain. Other close friends, including Canada, Australia, Germany and France, have pledged forces as the operation unfolds. More than 40 countries in the Middle East, Africa, Europe and across Asia have granted air transit or landing rights. Many more have shared intelligence . . .

More than two weeks ago, I gave Taliban leaders a series of clear and specific demands: Close terrorist training camps; hand over leaders of the al Qaeda network; and return all foreign nationals, including American citizens, unjustly detained in your country. None of these demands were met. And now the Taliban will pay a price. By destroying camps and disrupting communications, we will make it more difficult for the terror network to train new recruits and coordinate their evil plans.

Initially, the terrorists may burrow deeper into caves and other entrenched hiding places. Our military action is also designed to clear the way for sustained, comprehensive and relentless operations to drive them out and bring them to justice.

—President George W. Bush
Address to the Nation, October 7, 2001

---

1. Which country did the United States attack? Why was that country chosen as a target?

   _____

   _____

   _____

2. How did other nations help the United States in this operation?

   _____

   _____

   _____

Document-Based Activities

Activity 17   Document-Based Activity

The United States in Recent Times

DOCUMENT 3

Before You Read The following words in the document below may be
new to you: *infrastructure, synthesize, ad hoc.* You may want to use a
dictionary to look them up.

The President has proposed a new Department of Homeland Security.

The new department will be commissioned and tasked to protect our
borders and airports and seaports and to monitor visitors to this country; to
overseas preparedness and to help train and equip first-responders; to
address the threat from weapons of mass destruction, and turn policies into
action through regional drills; to map our Nation's critical infrastructure so
we can learn where the great vulnerabilities lie and take action to reduce
them; to synthesize and analyze homeland security intelligence from
multiple sources . . . and finally, to communicate threats and actions to
those who need to know—governors, mayors, law enforcement officials,
business owners, and the public . . .

Today, no single agency calls homeland security its sole or even its
primary mission. Instead, responsibility is scattered among more than 100
separate government organizations. Consequently, despite the best efforts
of the best public servants, our response is often ad hoc. We don't always
have the kind of alignment of authority and responsibility with
accountability that gets things done . . .

The Department of Homeland Security will have a single mission . . .
Protect the American people and our way of life from terrorism. And it will
have a single, clear line of authority to get the job done. It will bring
together everyone under the same roof, working toward the same goal and
pushing in the same direction.

—Tom Ridge, Office of Homeland Security Adviser
Address to the National Association of Broadcasters
National Education Foundation, June 10, 2002

---

1. What department was Homeland Security Adviser Tom Ridge promoting? What was
   its mission?

   _____

   _____

2. According to Ridge, what were the advantages of creating the new department?

   _____

   _____

Activity 17   Document-Based Activity

The United States in Recent Times

DOCUMENT 4
O'Hare International Airport
Chicago, Illinois, August 6, 2002

Getty Images

1. What are the Transportation Security Agency employees (the men on the left) doing?
   Why do you think they are doing so?

   _____

   _____

2. How do you think the airline passengers (the people on the right) feel about what is
   happening?

   _____

   _____

   _____

Document-Based Activity

The United States in Recent Times

DOCUMENT 5

Today, I will provide a brief summary of the Department's work to date implementing the new powers authorized by the USA PATRIOT Act . . .

First, the USA PATRIOT Act allowed us to modernize our badly outmoded surveillance tools . . . Prior to September 11, we operated both at a technological disadvantage and under legal barriers that severely restricted our surveillance capabilities. In particular, we did not have sufficiently sophisticated abilities to monitor communications . . . and law enforcement officials operated under . . . rules that hindered their ability to conduct investigations . . .

Second, the USA PATRIOT Act has removed various obstacles to investigating terrorism and has greatly enhanced the Department's ability to thwart, disrupt, weaken, and eliminate the infrastructure of terrorist organizations . . .

Third, the USA PATRIOT Act substantially strengthened criminal law, helping us pursue criminals in the most extensive criminal investigation in history . . . Title III of the USA PATRIOT Act provides law enforcement with important new authority to investigate and prosecute the financing of terrorism. We can now seize terrorist assets, both foreign and domestic, if the property or its owner is involved in, related to, or in support of acts of domestic or international terrorism . . .

Finally . . . the USA PATRIOT Act allowed us to significantly enhance our capability to share information and coordinate our efforts . . . Prior to last October, there was no mechanism for sharing certain types of criminal investigative material with the intelligence community, and the intelligence community could not easily open their files to law enforcement.

—Alice Fisher, deputy attorney general for the U.S. Dept. of Justice
Testimony before the Senate Committee on the Judiciary, October 9, 2002

1. How, according to deputy attorney general Alice Fisher, did the USA PATRIOT Act advance the fight against terrorism?

_____

_____

2. Why do you think some Americans opposed the PATRIOT Act?

_____

_____

Activity 17   Document-Based Activity

The United States in Recent Times

DOCUMENT 6

Before You Read The following words in the document below may be
new to you: *concerted*, *pariahs*. You may want to use a dictionary to look
them up.

> The international campaign against terrorism that President Bush launched
> and leads continues to be waged on every continent . . .
>
> I am pleased to report that unprecedented progress has been made across
> the international community. Nations everywhere now recognize that we
> are all in this together; none of us can combat terrorism alone . . .
> Concerted action is essential, and together we are taking that concerted
> action.
>
> Countries across the globe have taken concrete antiterrorism steps . . .
> The world's regional organizations have followed suit . . . United Nations
> sanctions have been imposed on many terrorist groups and on individuals,
> officially making these groups and individuals international pariahs.
>
> And here in the United States, we have designated additional groups and
> Foreign Terrorist Organizations. We and other members of the
> international community are sharing intelligence and law enforcement
> information and cooperating more closely than ever before, and we are
> working with our partners around the world to help them build their
> domestic capacities to combat the terrorist threat within and across their
> national boundaries . . .
>
> The financial bloodlines of terrorist organizations have been severed.
> Since [the September 11, 2001 terrorist attacks on the United States], more
> than $134 million of terrorist assets have been frozen. All around the
> world, countries have been tightening their border security and better
> safeguarding their critical infrastructures . . .
>
> —Colin L. Powell, U.S. Secretary of State
> Televised address, April 30, 2003

1. According to the document, how did other nations help the United States in its
   campaign against terrorism?

   _____

   _____

2. Why do you think international cooperation was so important to U.S. officials?

   _____

   _____

Activity 17 Document-Based Activity

The United States in Recent Times

DOCUMENT 7

Before You Read The following word in the document below may be new
to you: *proportionate*. You may want to use a dictionary to look it up.

Major combat operations in Iraq have ended. In the battle of Iraq, the
United States and our allies have prevailed . . .

In this battle, we have fought for the cause of liberty, and for the peace
of the world. Our nation and our coalition are proud of this
accomplishment – yet, it is you, the members of the United States military,
who achieved it . . . Because of you, our nation is more secure . . .

We have difficult work to do in Iraq. We're bringing order to parts of
that country that remain dangerous. We're pursuing and finding leaders of
the old regime, who will be held to account for their crimes. We've begun
the search for hidden chemical and biological weapons and already know
of hundreds of sites that will be investigated . . .

The liberation of Iraq is a crucial advance in the campaign against terror.
We've removed an ally of al Qaeda, and cut off a source of terrorist
funding. And this much is certain: No terrorist network will gain weapons
of mass destruction from the Iraqi regime, because the regime is no more.

In these 19 months that changed the world, our actions have been
focused and deliberate and proportionate to the offense. We have not
forgotten the victims of September the 11th . . . With those attacks, the
terrorists and their supporters declared war on the United States. And war
is what they got.

Our war against terror is proceeding according to principles that I have
made clear to all: Any person involved in committing or planning terrorist
attacks against the American people becomes an enemy of this country,
and a target of American justice.

—President George W. Bush
Announcing the end of major combat operations in Iraq, May 1, 2003

---

1. According to President George W. Bush, why did the United States invade Iraq?

   _____

   _____

2. How do you think the American people reacted to this announcement?

   _____

   _____

Activity 17

Document-Based Activity

The United States in Recent Times

Writing a Document-Based Essay

HISTORICAL CONTEXT On September 11, 2001, terrorists hijacked four passenger airliners. They piloted two of the jets into the twin towers of the World Trade Center in New York. Hijackers flew another airliner into the Pentagon building in Washington, D.C. Passengers stormed the cockpit of the fourth jet, causing it to crash in a field in Pennsylvania. The 9/11 attacks claimed nearly 3,000 lives and shocked the nation. President George W. Bush vowed to punish those responsible for the tragedy. The United States then launched a sweeping campaign against terrorism.

TASK Using information from the documents and your knowledge of American history, write an essay in which you:

- Describe the U.S. government's response to the 9/11 terrorist attacks.
- Explain how the U.S. government has tried to prevent future attacks against Americans.

Part B

DIRECTIONS Using the information from the documents provided and your knowledge of American history, write a well-organized essay that includes an introduction, a body of several paragraphs, and a conclusion. In the body of the essay, use examples from at least *four* documents. Support your response with relevant facts, examples, and details. Include additional outside information.

GUIDELINES
In your essay, be sure to:

- Address all aspects of the **Task** by accurately analyzing and interpreting at least *four* documents.
- Incorporate information from the documents in the body of the essay.
- Incorporate relevant outside information.
- Support the theme with relevant facts, examples, and details.
- Use a logical and clear plan of organization.
- Introduce the theme by establishing a framework that is beyond a simple statement of the **Task** or **Historical Context**.
- Conclude the essay with a summation of the theme.

Document-Based Activities

ACTIVITY 1: THE REVOLUTIONARY WAR

Document 1

Source *The American Revolutionaries: A History in Their Own Words 1750–1800.* Edited by Milton Meltzer. New York: Thomas Y. Crowell, 1987, pp. 63–64.

Document 2

Source *The American Revolution: Writings from the War of Independence.* Contents selected by John Rhodehamel. New York: The Library of America, 2001, pp. 223–224.

Document 3

Source *The American Revolutionaries: A History in Their Own Words 1750–1800.* Edited by Milton Meltzer. New York: Thomas Y. Crowell, 1987, pp. 109-110.

Document 4

Source *The American Revolution: Writings from the War of Independence.* Contents selected by John Rhodehamel. New York: The Library of America, 2001, pp. 301–302.

Document 5

Source *The American Revolution: Writings from the War of Independence.* Contents selected by John Rhodehamel. New York: The Library of America, 2001, pp. 414–415.

Document 6

Source *The American Revolution: Writings from the War of Independence.* Contents selected by John Rhodehamel. New York: The Library of America, 2001, pp. 671–672.

Document 7

Source *The American Revolution: Writings from the War of Independence.* Contents selected by John Rhodehamel. New York: The Library of America, 2001, pp. 744, 748.

ACTIVITY 2: DEBATING THE CONSTITUTION

Document 1

Source *The Debate on the Constitution: Federalist and Antifederalist Speeches, Articles, and Letters during the Struggle over Ratification*, Part One. Contents selected by Bernard Bailyn. New York: The Library of America, 1993, p. 15.

Document 2

Source *The Anti-Federalists: Selected Writings and Speeches.* Edited by Bruce Frohnen. Washington, DC: Regnery Publishing, Inc., 1999, p. 381.

Document 3

Source *The Anti-Federalists: Selected Writings and Speeches.* Edited by Bruce Frohnen. Washington, DC: Regnery Publishing, Inc., 1999, pp. 343, 345.

Document 4

Source *The Boisterous Sea of Liberty: A Documentary History of America from Discovery through the Civil War.* Edited by David Brion Davis and Steven Mintz. New York: Oxford University Press, 1999, p. 251.

Document 5

Source *The Anti-Federalists: Selected Writings and Speeches.* Edited by Bruce Frohnen. Washington, DC: Regnery Publishing, Inc., 1999, p. 338.

The Boisterous Sea of Liberty: A Documentary History of America from Discovery through the Civil War. Edited by David Brion Davis and Steven Mintz. New York: Oxford University Press, 1999, pp. 251–252.

Document 6

Source *The Boisterous Sea of Liberty: A Documentary History of America from Discovery through the Civil War.* Edited by David Brion Davis and Steven Mintz. New York: Oxford University Press, 1999, p. 252.

Document 7
Source *The Debate on the Constitution: Federalist and Antifederalist Speeches, Articles, and Letters during the Struggle over Ratification*, Part Two. Contents selected by Bernard Bailyn. New York: The Library of America, 1993, pp. 506, 512–513.

ACTIVITY 3: THE SECOND GREAT AWAKENING
Document 1
Source Barry Hankins, *The Second Great Awakening and the Transcendentalists*, Westport, CT: Greenwood Press, 2004, pp. 153–154.

Document 2
Source *The Way We Lived: Essays and Documents in American Social History*. Edited by Frederick M. Binder and David M. Reimers. Lexington, MA: D.C. Heath and Company, 1992, pp. 213–214.

Document 3
Source *The Radical Reader: A Documentary History of the American Radical Tradition*. Edited by Timothy Patrick McCarthy and John McMillian. New York: The New Press, 2003, pp. 67–68.

Document 4
Source *The Radical Reader: A Documentary History of the American Radical Tradition*. Edited by Timothy Patrick McCarthy and John McMillian. New York: The New Press, 2003, pp. 61–62.

Document 5
Source Barry Hankins, *The Second Great Awakening and the Transcendentalists*, Westport, CT: Greenwood Press, 2004, pp. 165–167.

Document 6
Source *The Radical Reader: A Documentary History of the American Radical Tradition*. Edited by Timothy Patrick McCarthy and John McMillian. New York: The New Press, 2003, pp. 138–140.

Document 7
Source Barry Hankins, *The Second Great Awakening and the Transcendentalists*, Westport, CT: Greenwood Press, 2004, pp. 169–170.

ACTIVITY 4: AFRICAN AMERICANS AND THE CIVIL WAR
Document 1
Source *A Documentary History of the Negro People in the United States,* Vol. 1, From Colonial Times through the Civil War. Edited by Herbert Aptheker. New York: The Citadel Press, 1968, pp. 470–471.

Document 2
Source *A Documentary History of the Negro People in the United States,* Vol. 1, From Colonial Times through the Civil War. Edited by Herbert Aptheker. New York: The Citadel Press, 1968, pp. 483–484.

Document 3
Source Peters Collection, Division of Social History, Domestic Life, National Museum of American History, Smithsonian Institution, Behring Center, Washington, D.C. http://www.civilwar.si.edu/soldiering_join_us.html

Document 4
Source Susie King Taylor, *A Black Woman's Civil War Memoirs*. Edited by Patricia W. Romero. New York: Markus Wiener Publishing, Inc., 1988, pp. 90–91.

Document 5
Source *A Grand Army of Black Men: Letters from African-American Soldiers in the Union Army, 1861–1865*. Edited by Edwin S. Redkey. New York: Cambridge University Press, 1992, pp. 272–273.

Document 6
Source *A Documentary History of the Negro People in the United States,* Vol. 1, From Colonial Times through the Civil War. Edited by Herbert Aptheker. New York: The Citadel Press, 1968, p. 487.

Document 7
Source James M. McPherson, *The Negro's Civil War: How American Negroes Felt and Acted during the War for the Union,* New York: Pantheon Books, 1965, pp. 231–232.

ACTIVITY 5: RECONSTRUCTION
Document 1
Source John Richard Dennett, *The South as It Is: 1865–1866.* Edited by Henry M. Christman. New York: Viking Press, 1965, p. 41.

Document 2
Source *The Boisterous Sea of Liberty: A Documentary History of America from Discovery through the Civil War.* Edited by David Brion Davis and Steven Mintz. New York: Oxford University Press, 1999, pp. 555–556.

Document 3
Source *The Reconstruction, A Documentary History of the South after the War: 1865–1877.* Edited by James P. Shenton. New York: G. P. Putnam's Sons, 1963, pp. 116–117.

Document 4
Source "Laws in Relation to Freedmen," U.S. Senate 39th Congress, 2nd Session, Senate Executive Document No. 6, pp. 96–97. http://memory.loc.gov/cgi-bin/query/r?ammem/aaodyssey:@field(NUMBER+@band(llmisc+ody0517))

Document 5
Source Picture History, Item 52.052 http://www.picturehistory.com/find/p/14619/mcms.html

Document 6
Source "Laws in Relation to Freedmen," U.S. Senate 39th Congress, 2nd Session, Senate Executive Document No. 6, pp. 75–76. http://memory.loc.gov/cgi-bin/query/r?ammem/aaodyssey:@field(NUMBER+@band(llmisc+ody0517))

Document 7
Source *A Documentary History of the Negro People in the United States,* Vol. 2, *From the Reconstruction Era to 1910.* Edited by Herbert Aptheker. New York: The Citadel Press, 1968, p. 594.

ACTIVITY 6: THE SECOND INDUSTRIAL REVOLUTION
Document 1
Source *Except to Walk Free: Documents and Notes in the History of American Labor.* Edited by Albert Fried. Garden City, NY: Anchor Books, 1974, p. 88.

Document 2
Source *Except to Walk Free: Documents and Notes in the History of American Labor.* Edited by Albert Fried. Garden City, NY: Anchor Books, 1974, pp. 111–118.

Document 3
Source *Except to Walk Free: Documents and Notes in the History of American Labor.* Edited by Albert Fried. Garden City, NY: Anchor Books, 1974, pp. 119–121.

Document 4
Source Georgia State University Library http://www.library.gsu.edu/spcoll/collections/av/19cLabor/19clabor04.htm

Document 5
Source Jacob Riis, *How the Other Half Lives: Studies among the Tenements of New York.* New York: Dover Publications, Inc., 1971, pp. 110–111.
Originally published in 1890 by Charles Scribner's Sons, New York.

Document 6
Source *Except to Walk Free: Documents and Notes in the History of American Labor.* Edited by Albert Fried. Garden City, NY: Anchor Books, 1974, pp. 157–159.

Document 7

Source *Except to Walk Free: Documents and Notes in the History of American Labor.* Edited by Albert Fried. Garden City, NY: Anchor Books, 1974, pp. 160–162.

ACTIVITY 7: THE WOMEN'S SUFFRAGE MOVEMENT
Document 1

Source *Women Together: A History in Documents of the Women's Movement in the United States.* Edited by Judith Papachristou. New York: Alfred A. Knopf, 1976, p. 144.

Document 2

Source *Women Together: A History in Documents of the Women's Movement in the United States.* Edited by Judith Papachristou. New York: Alfred A. Knopf, 1976, pp. 155–156.

Document 3

Source George Grantham Bain Collection, Library of Congress Prints and Photographs Division, Reproduction No. LC-USZ62-22262 DLC, Item 3: "Head of suffrage parade, Washington, D.C." http://memory.loc.gov/cgi-bin/query/ r?ammem/suffrg:@field(SUBJ+@band (Women's+suffrage--Washington++D+C ++--1910-1920+))

Document 4

Source *Women Together: A History in Documents of the Women's Movement in the United States.* Edited by Judith Papachristou. New York: Alfred A. Knopf, 1976, p. 176.

Document 5

Source Eleanor Flexner, *Century of Struggle: The Woman's Rights Movement in the United States,* revised edition. Cambridge, MA: The Belknap Press of Harvard University Press, 1975, pp. 290–291.

Document 6

Source National Archives and Records Administration, Records of the U.S. Senate, Record Group 46

http://www.archives.gov/education/lessons/ woman-suffrage/ny-petition.html

Document 7

Source *Women Together: A History in Documents of the Women's Movement in the United States.* Edited by Judith Papachristou. New York: Alfred A. Knopf, 1976, pp. 180–181, 182.

ACTIVITY 8: THE FIRST WORLD WAR
Document 1

Source From *The Myth of the Great War* by John Mosier. Copyright © 2001 by John Mosier. All rights reserved. Reproduced by permission of **HarperCollins, Inc.**

Document 2

Source John J. Pershing, *My Experiences in the World War,* Vol. 2. New York: Frederick A. Stokes Company, 1931, p. 68.

Document 3

Source Corbis, image no. IH170068 http://pro.corbis.com

Document 4

Source John J. Pershing, *My Experiences in the World War,* New York: Frederick A. Stokes Company, 1931, p. 205.

Document 5

Source *Eyewitness to America: 500 Years of America in the Words of Those Who Saw It Happen.* Edited by David Colbert. New York: Vintage Books, 1998, pp. 392–393.

Document 6

Source John J. Pershing, *My Experiences in the World War,* Vol. 2. New York: Frederick A. Stokes Company, 1931, pp. 272–273.

Document 7

Source William Mitchell, *Memoirs of World War I: "From Start to Finish of Our Greatest War,"* New York: Random House, 1960, pp. 275–277.

ACTIVITY 9: THE ROARING TWENTIES
Document 1
Source Cynthia Rose, project ed. *American Decades Primary Sources, 1920–1929.* Detroit: Gale, 2004, p. 93.

Document 2
Source From "Media and the Rise of Celebrity Culture" by Amy Henderson from *OAH Magazine of History,* No. 6, Spring 1992. Copyright © 1992 by **Organization of American Historians.** Reproduced by permission of the publisher.

Document 3
Source photograph: Dempsey–Carpentier fight. Corbis website: http://pro.corbis.com Image: BE053935

Document 4
Source Cynthia Rose, project ed. *American Decades Primary Sources, 1920–1929.* Detroit: Gale, 2004, pp. 453–454, 457.

Document 5
Source photography: premiere of *Hell's Angels.* University of Southern California Specialized Libraries and Archival Collections website:
http://www.usc.edu/isd/archives/arc/libraries/index.html
photograph URL:
http://www.usc.edu/isd/archives/arc/libraries/regional/photographs4.html

Document 6
Source From "New York Greets Lindbergh" by Oliver H. P. Garrett from *New York World,* May 22, 1927. Copyright 1927 by Oliver H. P. Garrett. Reproduced by permission of **the Estate of Oliver H. P. Garrett.**

Document 7
Source From "Ruth Crashed 60th to Set New Record" from *The New York Times,* October 1, 1927. Copyright 1927 by The New York Times. Reproduced by permission of **The New York Times Company.**

ACTIVITY 10: THE GREAT DEPRESSION
Document 1
Source From quote by Buddy Blankenship from *Hard Times: An Oral History of the Great Depression* by Studs Terkel. Copyright © 1970 by Studs Terkel. Reproduced by permission of **Donadio & Olson, Inc.**

Document 2
Source Quote by Louis Banks from *Hard Times: An Oral History of the Great Depression* by Studs Terkel. Copyright © 1970 by Studs Terkel. Reproduced by permission of **Donadio & Olson, Inc.**

Document 3
Source photo: Unemployed man sells an apple to Congressman Fred Hartley Corbis website: http://pro.corbis.com Image: U140872ACME

Document 4
Source Quote by Ben Isaacs from *Hard Times: An Oral History of the Great Depression* by Studs Terkel. Copyright © 1970 by Studs Terkel. Reproduced by permission of **Donadio & Olson, Inc.**

Document 5
Source photo: children at a Hooverville in Washington, D.C.
Getty Images website:
http://editorial.gettyimages.com/ms_gins/source/home/home.aspx?pg=1
Image: #2669031

Document 6
Source From "The Bronx Slave Market, 1935" by Ella Baker and Marvel Cooke from *The Crisis,* 42, November 1935. Copyright 1935 by **The Crisis.** Reproduced by permission of the publisher.

Document 7
Source From *Since Yesterday: The 1930s in America* by Frederick Lewis Allen. Copyright 1939, 1940 by Frederick Lewis Allen; copyright renewed © 1968 by Agnes Rogers Allen. All

rights reserved. Reproduced by permission of **HarperCollins Publishers, Inc.**

ACTIVITY 11: THE NEW DEAL
Document 1
Source *Down and Out in the Great Depression: Letters from the "Forgotten Man."* Edited by Robert S. McElvaine. Chapel Hill, NC: University of North Carolina Press, 1983, p. 133.

Document 2
Source From "Why Business Men Fear Washington" by W. M. Kiplinger from *Scribner's,* October 1934. Copyright 1934 by W. M. Kiplinger. Reproduced by permission of **Kiplinger Washington.**

Document 3
Source *Huey Long.* Edited by Hugh Davis Graham. Englewood Cliffs, NJ: Prentice-Hall, Inc., 1970, pp. 71–72.

Document 4
Source From "Roosevelt and Ruin" radio address by Father Charles E. Coughlin, June 19, 1936. Accessed at www.pbs.org.greatspeeches.

Document 5
Source *Down and Out in the Great Depression: Letters from the "Forgotten Man."* Edited by Robert S. McElvaine. Chapel Hill, NC: University of North Carolina Press, 1983, pp. 145–147.

Document 6
Source cartoon: "What Next?" found at the New Deal Network website: http://newdeal.feri.org/default.cfm cartoon url: http://newdeal.feri.org/texts/161.htm

Document 7
Source Statement by Frank E. Gannett, National Archives and Records Administration, Records of the Justice Department, Record Group 60, found at the

National Archives Teaching With Documents website: http://www.archives.gov/education/lessons/ document url: http://www.archives.gov/education/lessons/ separation-powers/

ACTIVITY 12: THE U.S. RESPONSE TO THE HOLOCAUST
Document 1
Source Memo from Assistant Secretary of State Breckinridge Long, to State Department Officials dated June 26, 1940, outlining effective ways to obstruct the granting of U.S. visas. http://www.pbs.org/wgbh/amex/holocaust/film more/reference/primary/barmemo.html

Document 2
Source People and Events: Breckinridge Long (1881–1958) http://www.pbs.org/wgbh/amex/holocaust/ peopleevents/pandeAMEX90.html

Document 3
Source *Witness to the Holocaust.* Edited by Michael Berenbaum, New York: HarperCollins, 1997, p. 252. Timeline of America's reaction to the Holocaust: 1933–1940 web site: http://www.pbs.org/wgbh/amex/holocaust/ timeline/index.html Timeline of America's reaction to the Holocaust: 1941–1942 web site: http://www.pbs.org/wgbh/amex/holocaust/ timeline/index_2.html *American Anthem*, Austin, TX: Holt, Rinehart and Winston, 2007, p. 779–780. William L. Shirer, *The Rise and Fall of the Third Reich: A History of Nazi Germany*, New York: Simon and Schuster, 1988, p. 964.

Document 4
Source *Witness to the Holocaust.* Edited by Michael Berenbaum, New York: HarperCollins, 1997, pp. 261–262.

Document 5
Source John J. McCloy, Assistant Secretary of War, explains to John W. Pehle, Director, War Refugee Board, that the War Department cannot authorize the bombing of Auschwitz, November 18, 1944.
web site:
http://www.pbs.org/wgbh/amex/holocaust/filmmore/reference/primary/bombjohn.html

Document 6
Source David S. Wyman, *The Abandonment of the Jews: America and the Holocaust 1941–1945*, New York: Pantheon Books, 1984, pp. 296, 299–300.

Document 7
Source "Survivors in Mauthausen open one of the crematoria ovens for American troops who are inspecting the camp," Photo 77019, United States Holocaust Memorial Museum.

ACTIVITY 13: THE KOREAN WAR
Document 1
Source Cynthia Rose, project ed. *American Decades Primary Sources, 1950-1959.* Detroit: Gale, 2004, p. 215.

Document 2
Source *Encyclopedia of the Korean War,* Vol. 3. Edited by Spencer C. Tucker. Santa Barbara, CA: ABC-CLIO, Inc., 2000, pp. 875–876.

Document 3
Source *Encyclopedia of the Korean War,* Vol. 3. Edited by Spencer C. Tucker. Santa Barbara, CA: ABC-CLIO, Inc., 2000, pp. 926–927.

Document 4
Source From *War in Korea: The Report of a Woman Combat Correspondent* by Marguerite Higgins. Copyright 1951 by Marguerite Higgins. Reproduced by permission of **Doubleday, a division of Random House, Inc., www.randomhouse.com.**

Document 5
Source Map of Communist Advances in East Asia
Corbis website: http://pro.corbis.com
Image: U954934ACME

Document 6
Source *Encyclopedia of the Korean War,* Vol. 3. Edited by Spencer C. Tucker. Santa Barbara, CA: ABC-CLIO, Inc., 2000, p. 981.

Document 7
Source *Encyclopedia of the Korean War,* Vol. 3. Edited by Spencer C. Tucker. Santa Barbara, CA: ABC-CLIO, Inc., 2000, p. 996.

ACTIVITY 14: THE CIVIL RIGHTS MOVEMENT
Document 1
Source From *Revolutionary Suicide* by Huey P. Newton, with the assistance of J. Herman Blake. Copyright © 1973 by Huey P. Newton. Reproduced by permission of **Harcourt, Inc.**

Document 2
Source Quotes by Linda Bryant Hall and Bob Lucas from *Voices of Freedom: An Oral History of the Civil Rights Movement from the 1950s Through the 1980s,* edited by Henry Hampton and Steve Fayer. Copyright © 1990 by Blackside, Inc. Reproduced by permission of **Bantam Books, a division of Random House, Inc., www.randomhouse.com.**

Document 3
Source Police Arresting Looters During 1967 Newark Riots
Corbis website: http://pro.corbis.com
Image: BE020706

Document 4
Source *Let Freedom Ring: A Documentary History of the Modern Civil Rights Movement.* Edited by Peter B. Levy. New York: Praeger Publishers, 1992, pp. 191–192.

Document 5
Source From "Beyond Vietnam" by Martin Luther King, Jr. Copyright © 1967 by Martin Luther King, Jr.; copyright renewed 1995 by Coretta Scott King. Reproduced by permission of the **Estate of Martin Luther King, Jr., c/o Writer's House as agent for the proprietor New York, NY.**

Document 6
Source Quotes by Harry Belafonte and Kathleen Neal Cleaver from *Voices of Freedom: An Oral History of the Civil Rights Movement from the 1950s Through the 1980s,* edited by Henry Hampton and Steve Fayer. Copyright © 1990 by Blackside, Inc. Reproduced by permission of **Bantam Books, a division of Random House, Inc., www.randomhouse.com.**

Document 7
Source *Let Freedom Ring: A Documentary History of the Modern Civil Rights Movement.* Edited by Peter B. Levy. New York: Praeger Publishers, 1992, pp. 220–222.

ACTIVITY 15: THE VIETNAM WAR
Document 1
Source *The Vietnam War: Primary Sources.* Edited by David M. Haugen. San Diego, CA: Lucent Books, 2002, pp. 20–21.

Document 2
Source From *"Who Was Lyndon Baines Johnson"* by Doris Kearns from *The Atlantic Monthly,* July 1976. Copyright © 1976 by Doris Kearns. Reproduced by permission of the author.

Document 3
Source Cynthia Rose, project ed. *American Decades Primary Sources, 1960-1969.* Detroit: Gale, 2004, pp. 266–268.

Document 4
Source watergate.info website
http://watergate.info/
Document URL:

http://watergate.info/nixon/silent-majority-speech-1969.shtml

Document 5
Source Photo: Students Protesting Outside White House
Corbis website: http://pro.corbis.com
Image: 0000403896-002

Document 6
Source From "U.S. to Tighten Surveillance of Radicals" by James Naughton from *The New York Times,* April 12, 1970. Copyright © 1970 by The New York Times. Reproduced by permission of **The New York Times Company.**

Document 7
Source The Avalon Project at Yale Law School website
http://www.yale.edu/lawweb/avalon/
Document URL:
http://www.yale.edu/lawweb/avalon/warpower.htm

ACTIVITY 16: THE REAGAN ERA
Document 1
Source National Center for Public Policy Research website:
http://www.nationalcenter.org/index.html
Document URL:
http://www.nationalcenter.org/ReaganEvilEmpire1983.html

Document 2
Source Reagan 2020 website:
http://reagan2020.us/
Document URL:
http://reagan2020.us/speeches/Defense_and_Security.asp

Document 3
Source Constantine C. Menges, *Inside the National Security Council: The True Story of the Making and Unmaking of Reagan's Foreign Policy*, New York: Simon and Schuster, 1988, pp. 88–89.

Document 4

Source Photo: Marines Carrying a Body in Beirut
Corbis website: http://pro.corbis.com
Image: BE023465

Document 5

Source George P. Shultz, *Turmoil and Triumph: My Years as Secretary of State*, New York: Charles Scribner's Sons, 1993, pp. 686–687.

Document 6

Source *Report of the Congressional Committees Investigating the Iran-Contra Affair*, Abridged Edition. Edited by Joel Brinkley and Stephen Engelberg. New York: Times Books, 1988, pp. 21–23.

Document 7

Source Ronald Reagan Presidential Library website: http://www.reagan.utexas.edu/
Document URL:
http://www.reagan.utexas.edu/archives/speeches/1987/121087a.htm

ACTIVITY 17: THE UNITED STATES IN RECENT TIMES

Document 1

Source *The 9/11 Commission Report: Final Report of the National Commission on Terrorist Attacks Upon the United States*, Authorized Edition, New York: W.W. Norton and Company, 2004, p. 327.

Document 2

Source The Avalon Project at Yale Law School website:
http://www.yale.edu/lawweb/avalon/
Document URL:
http://www.yale.edu/lawweb/avalon/sept_11/president_035.htm

Document 3

Source *The War on Terrorism: Opposing Viewpoints*. Edited by Karen F. Balkin, Farmington Hills. MI: Greenhaven Press, 2005, pp. 108–110.

Document 4

Source Photo: Federal Workers Man Security Posts at O'Hare
Getty Images website:
http://creative.gettyimages.com/source/home/home.aspx
Image #1297012

Document 5

Source *Homeland Security*. Edited by James D. Torr. Farmington Hills, MI: Greenhaven Press, 2004, pp. 34–41.

Document 6

Source *The War on Terrorism: Opposing Viewpoints*. Edited by Karen F. Balkin. Farmington Hills, MI: Greenhaven Press, 2005, pp. 165–166.

Document 7

Source AMDOCS Documents for the Study of American History website:
http://www.ku.edu/carrie/docs/amdocs_index.html
Document URL:
http://www.ku.edu/carrie/docs/texts/bush 052003.html

SCORING ESSAYS

This rubric is designed to help evaluate student essays.

For a score of 5, student

- shows a complete understanding of the question or theme
- states the theme or problem clearly in his or her own words
- addresses all aspects of the task
- demonstrates an ability to analyze, evaluate, and compare and contrast issues and events
- supports the theme or question by using many relevant facts, examples, and details
- provides information in a well organized and logical way
- uses at least four of the documents to create the essay

For a score of 4, student

- shows a good understanding of the question or theme
- states the theme or problem clearly in his or her own words
- addresses most aspects of the task
- demonstrates an ability to analyze, evaluate, and compare and contrast issues and events
- uses relevant facts, examples, and details
- provides information in a well-organized and logical way
- uses three documents to create the essay

For a score of 3, student

- shows a satisfactory understanding of the question or theme
- states the theme or problem by repeating similar examples
- addresses most aspect of the task, but glosses over some details
- demonstrates an ability to analyze issues and events, but not in depth

- uses some relevant facts, examples, and details
- provides information in a generally organized way
- uses two documents to create the essay

For a score of 2, student

- shows limited understanding of the question or theme
- fails to state the theme or problem
- attempts to address the task
- demonstrates an illogical analysis of issues and events
- includes few facts, examples, or details; introduces some errors
- provides information that is poorly organized
- uses one document to create the essay

For a score of 1, student

- shows a very limited understanding of the question or theme
- fails to state the theme or problem
- attempts to address the task
- lacks any analysis of issues and events
- includes few facts, examples, or details; introduces many errors
- provides information with little or no organization
- uses no documents

For a score of 0, student

- fails to complete any of the tasks satisfactorily, work is illegible, or paper is blank

SCORING CONSTRUCTED RESPONSE QUESTIONS

The student workbook contains constructed response questions following each document. This rubric shows how constructed response questions are graded.

- **Questions that have only <u>one</u> correct answer:** Questions that have only one correct answer can earn a maximum of one point. Students who answer the question correctly earn one point. Those who answer incorrectly or not at all earn zero points. A correct response that is copied directly from a passage or that is paraphrased from a passage should receive full credit.

- **Questions that require <u>more than one</u> answer:** Some questions have more than one part. Such questions can earn a maximum of two points. Students who answer both parts correctly get two points. Students who answer only one part, but get it right, earn one point. Students who answer incorrectly or not at all earn zero points. A correct response that is copied directly from a passage or that is paraphrased from a passage should receive full credit.

For both types of constructed response items, students do not need to answer the question in complete sentences to receive full credit. However, by answering the questions using complete sentences, students will begin to develop the writing fluency they will need to complete the essay at the end of each activity.